CHOOSING A

Family Reference titles in this Series

Be a Local Councillor
Be an Effective School Governor
Becoming a Father
Cash from your Computer
Choose a Private School
Choosing a Nursing Home
Choosing a Package Holiday
Claim State Benefits
Dealing with your Bank
Dealing with a Death in the Family
Having a Baby
Helping your Child to Read
Lose Weight & Keep Fit
Make a Complaint
Making a Wedding Speech
Managing your Personal Finances
Plan a Wedding
Prepare your Child for School
Raise Funds & Sponsorship
Run a Local Campaign
Run a Voluntary Group
Successful Grandparenting
Successful Single Parenting
Survive Divorce
Take Care of your Heart
Taking in Students
Use the Internet
Teaching Someone to Drive
Winning Consumer Competitions

Other titles in preparation

The How To series now contains more than 170 titles in the following categories:

Business Basics
Family Reference
Jobs & Careers
Living & Working Abroad
Student Handbooks
Successful Writing

Please send for a free copy of the latest catalogue for full details.

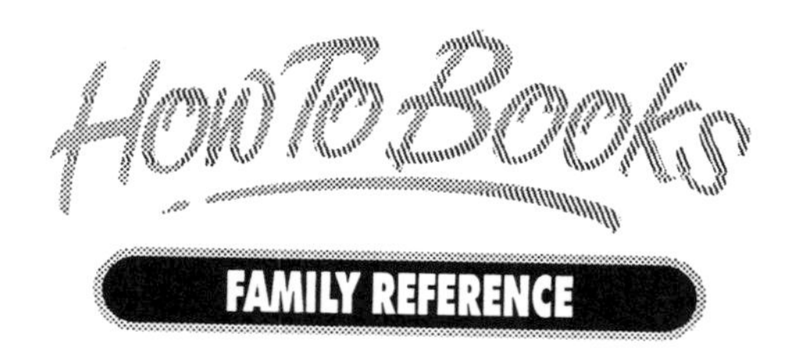

CHOOSING A NURSING HOME

How to arrange the right long-term care for an elderly dependent or relative

Mary Webb

How To Books

Cartoons by Mike Flanagan

British Library Cataloguing in Publication Data
A catalogue record for this book is available from the British Library.

First published in 1996 by How To Books Ltd, Plymbridge House, Estover Road, Plymouth PL6 7PZ, United Kingdom. Tel: (01752) 202301. Fax: (01752) 202331.

Note: The material contained in this book is set out in good faith for general guidance and no liability can be accepted for loss or expense incurred as a result of relying in particular circumstances on statements made in the book. The laws and regulations are complex and liable to change, and readers should check the current position with the relevant authorities before making personal arrangements.

Produced for How To Books by Deer Park Productions.
Typeset by The Baskerville Press, Salisbury, Wiltshire.
Printed and bound by Cromwell Press, Broughton Gifford, Melksham, Wiltshire.

Contents

List of Illustrations

Preface

There are many hundreds of Care Homes around the country, all caring for people with different abilities, in different age groups and from differing backgrounds. How do you choose which one is most suitable for your relative when they can no longer care for themselves?

This book will help you to choose the most suitable home for your relative and ways in which you can make the transition a little easier for them.

My special thanks to everyone who has helped and supported me in this venture: my husband Roy and daughters Dawn and Lyn. All have given me their approval and encouragement.

Writers: Norman Toulson, Dianna Lloyd Taylor and Clare Gill for proofreading and constructive criticism.

May Graves, Chris Belton and Pat Reid who helped to verify the facts and made suggestions.

Bob, Al, Elaine and Kim at Donnelly Gunn, Nursing Home Operators, who supplied the sample contract.

Extra special thanks to Christine Hall, proprietor of Scriptease Editorial and author of several books. Without Christine's help and encouragement the book might never have been written.

The characters and organisations in the case studies are fictitious. They have been created to demonstrate typical situations. Any similarity to real people or organisations is entirely coincidental. All charts, letters and other documents (unless marked) are samples written especially to demonstrate a similar document.

Mary Webb

IS THIS YOU?

Son Daughter Spouse

Partner Brother

Sister In-law Cousin

Family friend Neighbour

Relative Practice nurse Social worker

Solicitor Accountant

Community nurse GP Bank manager

Care assistant Citizens Advice Bureau

Benefits officer Health worker Counsellor

Occupational therapist Matron

Minister Samaritan Priest

Community worker Voluntary worker

Financial adviser Council officer Hospice staff

Befriender

1
Starting from Scratch

CONSIDERING YOUR RELATIVE'S NEEDS

Before choosing the nursing home that will be your relative's new home take time to assess their basic needs. Later, consider the type of person they are, their preferences and pet hates. Time taken to make such an evaluation will help you to choose the home most suited to them.

- Coping with inconveniences on holiday for two weeks is easy.
- Living permanently with inconveniences can be like a prison sentence.

Distractions

There are many pleasant distractions to compensate for the shortcomings of holiday accommodation. However, if your relative is to create a home in their new surroundings it needs to be as near to their liking as possible.

Finding out what they need

Some people may find the easiest way to assess their relative is to make a list under four headings:

Physical

For example, general health, mobility and the type of help they now need to live as normal a life as possible.

Psychological

For example, memory loss, confusion plus other more serious problems.

Spiritual

For example, their religious persuasion. Whether they are active members of their church. Would they like to receive pastoral visits or communion?

Social

For example, are they a shy or outgoing person? Do they make friends easily? Are they a member of a luncheon club or group perhaps?

You could make a chart to help give you a profile of your relative and their needs. However, to get an accurate picture, all your information must be correct. The chart shown in Figure 1 is only an example. You will probably think of other things to add.

SEEING THE DOCTOR

If you feel that your relative needs residential nursing care you should first discuss the matter with their doctor. You will be asked why you think such care is needed. Don't be embarrassed if you are the carer and are finding it too much for you to cope with. Doctors do realise what a strain it can be to look after a sick or elderly person without proper support. However, unless you give them all the facts they may not be able to offer help.

Visiting the surgery

If your relative is mobile and able to get to the surgery take them to see the doctor. Doctors generally prefer to see patients in the surgery if at all possible.

Asking questions

Make a list of all the things you want to ask. Many people forget to ask the questions they want answers to when they actually get into the surgery. You may want to ask about:

- the current problems
- involvement of a care manager
- residential/nursing care
- physical/mental assessment.

Physical health problem	Needs
Poor mobility	Help with walking
Incontinence	Frequent visits to the toilet Incontinence pads
Diabetic	Insulin injections Diabetic diet Chiropody Eye examinations
Psychological problems	
None	
Spiritual	
Member of Baptist Church	Minister needs to be contacted
Social activities	
Member of Bridge Club	Room to invite friends for bridge
Enjoys reading	Introduce them to in-house library Introduce them to other readers

Fig. 1. Sample chart of needs.

Asking for a visit

Telephone the surgery and ask for the doctor to visit and assess your relative at home if:

- they have not been seen for some time and need assessment
- their condition has deteriorated
- the carer(s) can no longer cope.

Take this opportunity to ask questions about:

- your relative's state of health
- prognosis
- admission to hospital for treatment, rehabilitation and assessment
- future care
- referral to a care manager.

Getting a second opinion

If you feel the answers you are getting are unsatisfactory you can ask for your relative to be referred to an appropriate specialist – for example, a geriatrician, an expert in assessing and rehabilitating elderly people. However, doctors will automatically make a referral if they think it is necessary.

Once the referral has been made your relative will be offered the first available appointment at the nearest hospital. If, due to frailty, illness or poor mobility they are unable to keep the appointment, phone the hospital; they may be able to arrange transport. Sometimes it is possible for the consultant to make a domiciliary visit. If neither of these options is feasible go back to the surgery and ask for assistance.

Going into hospital

Because it is impossible to do a complete assessment of a patient in an hour or two the consultant may admit them for a few days. During their stay all aspects of their health, mobility, medication and mental state are observed.

Testing, testing, testing!

A series of tests may be carried out, such as:

- ECG (heart trace)

- X-rays
- blood tests
- urine tests
- mobility may be assessed by the physiotherapist
- co-ordination and ability tests may be carried out by the occupational therapist
- medication will be reviewed and possibly changed.

When all assessments and treatments are completed the consultant will be able to make a decision about your relative's future care.

Many patients' health and mobility improve whilst in hospital: they return home able to cope, with full back-up from the Social Services. Unfortunately the improvements are not always maintained and a second referral may have to be made.

CONTACTING THE CARE MANAGER

There are three main ways in which you can contact the care manager:

- ask the doctor for a referral
- phone the care manager's office
- ask ward staff (if the patient is in hospital) for a referral.

Every doctor's practice has an affiliated care manager. At some practices care managers hold 'clinics' for the patients' benefit. Ring the surgery for details.

Meeting the care manager

The initial meeting between you and the care manager may take place in the doctor's surgery, the care manager's office, the hospital or your relative's own home.

Assessing your relative

Care managers assist in the assessment of needs of persons who are unable to care for themselves. Clients' needs vary from minimal support to total care. After consulting with the family, the care manager will arrange for your relative to receive an appropriate amount of help and care.

Depending on the assessment, this may be:

- in their own home
- residential care
- nursing home care in an appropriate home.

You must be able to tell the care manager what you think your relative needs to enable them to cope with their disabilities. It's sometimes difficult to remember everything at the time, so why not make a list? You could also show them your own assessment you have made.

Care needs

The care manager will discuss your relative's needs and the amount and type of care required with your relative and yourself. They will ask about:

- your relative's current problems
- medical problems
- ability to care for themselves
- present care arrangements
- why the present arrangements need to be changed
- anything else that may be relevant.

Final decisions regarding admission to a nursing home cannot be made until your doctor has been consulted, assessment made, paperwork finished and authorisation from the local authority obtained. This can take several days to complete.

Emergency admissions

In an emergency your relative can be placed in a nursing home by their doctor and reviewed as soon as possible after their admission. This is generally only allowed during weekends and bank holidays.

Assessing financial need

Providing there is no danger of your relative's money running out whilst they still need nursing or residential care you can make your own arrangements. You can discuss their requirements and arrange their admission with the matron of the chosen home without involving a care manager.

Most people, however, will need financial assistance either from the date of admission or later when their bank balance has dropped to £16,000.

Residential nursing care is expensive, making longterm care beyond most people's income. If there is any possibility that assistance will be needed, either immediately or in the future, it is advisable to involve their care manager at the start. They will:

- assess your relative's current needs – which may differ from your own assessment
- advise you on the type of care needed (residential or nursing)
- tell you what is available
- give you a list of homes in the area.

Choosing not to involve the care manager

You are not obliged to involve a care manager if your relative has sufficient funds to pay their own fees for a limited period of time. However, there are a couple of things you should be aware of:

1. The care manager's assessment of your relative may differ from your own assessment of their needs.

2. When your relative's funds run out you could be asked to transfer them to a more appropriate home if, for instance, they had been placed in a nursing home when they could be cared for in a residential home.

3. It may be difficult to obtain sufficient financial help to continue their care in the home of their choice.

4. The home in which they have been placed may not have a contract with the local authority.

To qualify for financial help your relative will have a financial assessment carried out by the care manager (see Chapter 5, page 61, Paying the bills).

Respite care

Some clients can afford periods of respite care in a nursing home without getting into financial difficulty. When they have insufficient funds to pay for this type of care, approach the care manager for advice. If it is deemed to be a necessity they may be able to obtain funding from the local authority.

Getting a list of local homes

There are several ways of getting to know where the homes are:

- asking your care manager for the current list
- home finding agencies
- the *Yellow Pages*
- *Thomsons Directory*
- *Directory of Nursing Homes* (reference section in the library)
- Nursing Homes Inspectorate (Community Health Department listed under the local Health Authority in the phone directory)
- local paper advertisements
- promotional functions and literature issued by nursing homes
- by noticing their own sign boards at the front of the house
- personal recommendation.

Obtaining information

You can telephone the home for a brochure and information. If possible, speak to the matron – this gives you a chance to ask basic questions, for example:

- Are there any vacancies?
- In private rooms?
- In contracted rooms?

It will give you the opportunity to discover the matron's attitude: is he/she friendly, helpful, interested? You may like to view the home at this stage.

Sometimes it is better to write for information.

What to ask for

- two brochures, one for your relative and one for yourself
- list of fees
- directions to the home if required

- if there are any vacancies
- what category of residents they are registered to care for (nursing, EMI (Elderly Mentally Ill), residential)
- any other information you need.

The advantage of writing is that you receive the information in black and white, thus avoiding misunderstandings.

Recommendations

The best recommendations you can have are from residents and their families who have had experience of a particular home. They will usually tell you everything you need to know from a resident's viewpoint.

They don't need prompting to tell you if the food is awful or if residents are left for long periods of time without attention. But beware, sometimes fantasy, imagination and distortion of fact can creep into a conversation.

One person's view of a home may not be typical when compared with other people's opinion. Where possible, get more than one opinion of a home.

Doctors visit nursing homes if they have patients who are residents. They might tell you whether they are well cared for but may be unable to give any other details.

Health authority inspectors, home finding agencies and care managers are not allowed to make their preferences known.

CHECKLIST

- Have you listed your relative's needs?
- Have you sent for the brochures?
- Have you asked other people if they can recommend a home?

CASE STUDIES – INTRODUCTION

Mavis becomes responsible for her father

Mavis Pike is 35. She is an attractive woman with three children aged five, eight and 13. Her husband died in a road accident when the youngest child was two.

She works as a hairdresser to support herself and the children. The house was paid for by insurance when her husband died. Although she is competent and well liked she lacks confidence and is an anxious person.

Mavis has no relatives other than her father, her 32-year-old sister Julia and her children. Three months ago her mother died following a severe stroke, leaving her husband, Peter Andrews, aged 70 on his own.

Peter needs help

Since his bereavement Peter Andrews has neglected himself. Mavis and Julia have taken him hot meals which he refused. He exists on cold milk and biscuits. He does not wash or shave and is reluctant to change his clothing. The two sisters clean the house and wash his clothing when he will allow.

Peter was a coal miner and was trapped underground for three days following a pit explosion. Although it was over 50 years ago he still has occasional nightmares.

He is frail, weak, unstable and suffers from short-term memory loss and intermittent mild confusion. He is currently in hospital undergoing treatment for a fractured femur resulting from a fall.

Alan worries about his wife

Alan Bright is 46. He is married to 43-year-old Peggy, who suffers from multiple sclerosis (MS).

They have two adult children, Avril at university and Mark, who is working abroad.

Alan is a carpenter working for a firm of builders specialising in building exclusive top-of-the-range houses. His firm think highly of him and frequently send him away to work on specialised projects. When this happens he can be away for several weeks at a time.

He is concerned about his wife Peggy. He has engaged agency nurses to look after her, but the situation is far from satisfactory and is extremely costly. Alan is scheduled to work on a Scottish project and is due to leave in four weeks' time.

Peggy has a deteriorating condition

Peggy Bright developed a urinary infection after the birth of her daughter. When the infection cleared she still felt dizzy and nauseated and realised she had some weakness in her legs. After tests her condition was diagnosed as multiple sclerosis.

Her symptoms cleared slowly. She was told she could be in remission for several years. Peggy remained healthy until she was 35 and then succumbed to several concurrent infections which exacerbated the disease. This gradually impaired her mobility until most of her waking hours were spent in a wheelchair.

During the past year Peggy has become totally dependent on others for all aspects of daily living. She has partial use of her left hand plus two fingers on her right hand. She can speak but her voice fades when she tires.

Peggy sleeps on a special bed that helps to prevent pressure sores, but a week ago she developed a small open sore on her left hip. This has become large and infected. The community nurses have been treating and dressing the sore.

Connie becomes forgetful

Audrey West's favourite auntie, Connie Crisp, lives in Madrid. She emigrated to Spain 20 years ago when she retired. She is now 80 and has no other relatives.

Recently Audrey received a phone call from her aunt's next-door neighbour telling her she is unfit to live alone. Connie frequently gets lost and wanders in the streets, causing havoc as she walks among the traffic. She forgets to turn off her electrical appliances, burning herself on more than one occasion. She has become a danger to herself and others.

Audrey agreed to visit her aunt and make arrangements for her future care. Her husband is a freelance journalist and uses the spare bedroom as an office. Audrey works in market research and is out most evenings and weekends.

Initially Audrey thought that it might be better to leave her aunt in Spain with a companion. After thinking about it she decided to assess the amount and type of care her aunt needed while she stayed in Madrid. Audrey is now travelling to Spain.

Frederick has cancer

Fred, aged 72, is blind and suffering from cancer of the bowel. Six months ago he underwent surgery and now has a colostomy. He has recovered but is quite frail and unable to manage his colostomy. He is married to Annie, aged 70.

Annie suffers a heart attack

Annie Drew cares for her husband and their 30-year-old son, Kevin, who has learning difficulties.

This morning Annie suffered a myocardial infarction (heart attack) and has been taken to hospital. Neighbours are looking after Kevin and Fred until other arrangements can be made. Annie has an older brother who is being cared for in a nursing home several miles away. There are no other relatives.

Both Annie and Fred are members of the local Baptist Church. They are a popular couple and have many friends. Their special friend is Elizabeth, the choir leader.

DISCUSSION POINTS

1. What kind of a person is your relative?
2. What type of home are you looking for?
3. What are your relative's needs?
4. What can your relative do without?

2
Considering Feelings

COPING WITH RESERVATIONS

How would you feel if you were told that you could no longer live at home?

Most people know when they really can't look after themselves any longer but tend to put off seeking help. It is disturbing for them when they finally call their doctor and are admitted to hospital for care and rehabilitation. Most patients do their best to regain the skills they once had, thinking they will soon be discharged home again.

Managing rehabilitation

Weeks may be spent in a rehabilitation unit carrying out tasks to assess their mental ability and physical dexterity. They will undergo tests which inform the consultant how well their body is functioning. Physiotherapy might be given to strengthen muscles they didn't know they had. Medications could be changed to see if one has a better effect than a previous one.

They will have to get used to being with other people for 24 hours a day, eating together and sleeping in the ward together: sometimes they are put into mixed wards. If a person is a 'loner' this can be very traumatic for them. Many elderly people feel shy at having to sleep in a room with the opposite sex. Others respond and become brighter, instinctively making the most of themselves in this situation.

Fluctuating moods

Whatever kind of person they are, being admitted into hospital for illness or rehabilitation will affect their moods. On a bad day they may be disgruntled, irritable or even aggressive. On a good day they may be hopeful and optimistic – and frustrated on the days when they hear the consultant say, 'I will see you next week'.

Hearing the decision

Then comes that awful day when they are told they can't return home but have to be cared for in a nursing home. The stiff upper lip is held until the consultant leaves, then worrying starts and tears flow.

WHAT THE INDIVIDUAL MIGHT BE FEELING

Feelings will probably be a mixture of positive and negative depending on the person's current mood.

Negative feelings

- fear of the unknown
- uselessness, in that they are no longer able to 'earn their keep'
- being a burden, feeling they are an encumbrance to their family and society
- despair, that they are no longer wanted
- suicidal, sometimes feeling that they would be better off dead.

Suicidal thoughts are only expressed by a few people. However, because a person never tells you they're thinking of suicide doesn't mean that they don't have them.

Fortunately not everybody feels this way. Many feel positive.

Positive feelings

- relief at not having to cope with the stress of daily living
- anticipation of an easier life
- hope for new friends and companionship
- freedom from financial worries.

Accepting the inevitable

It may take considerable skill on your part to help your relative to accept their transfer from hospital to another caring environment such as a nursing home. Try:

- talking to them to ascertain what their worries are
- reassuring them that if they're unhappy they can try another home

- accentuating the positive side of things
- involving them as much as possible in the choice of home
- arranging for them to visit the home on a trial basis
- discussing with them what they want to take into the home
- offering to have a telephone installed if this is possible
- contacting friends and relatives to arrange visiting
- allaying their fears by discussing delicate issues (toileting, privacy and personal hygiene) and sleeping arrangements with them and staff
- making them realise they could return home if their physical capabilities improve enough for them to care for themselves.

CONSIDERING PARTNERS

A few years ago married couples were the only people considered to have partners. Nowadays, an unmarried person may have a partner who needs to be considered. If two people are living together as close friends, for companionship or in a homosexual relationship, they need to be consulted. Their feelings will be the same as a married partner and they will be the one person the resident will want to visit them. This is sometimes hard for other people to accept.

Consulting their partner

It's not only the unattached person who needs to be admitted into a nursing home. Sometimes partners are left to carry on their own life whilst their loved one is being cared for in a residential establishment. This can happen when one partner has a stroke, a disabling accident or an exacerbation of a chronic disease.

The partner's attitude

The attitude of the partner left alone will be coloured by the feelings the couple have for one another. For instance, if they have always loved and cared for each other, the partner will feel they want to and can still look after their loved one. They need persuading that it is impracticable or that they are too frail themselves to continue giving longterm care.

On the other hand, if the partnership has been one of a martyred existence, the enforced separation may produce relief or even pleasure.

The partner's reaction and feelings

- shock - of partner's illness and need for nursing home care
- anger - at God, the children or anybody who is enforcing separation
- guilt - because they are unable to give the necessary care
- relief - because their partner will get the care they deserve
- fear - they will be unable to visit
  - they will have no say in their partner's care
  - they will be lonely and unable to look after themselves
  - their beloved partner will never return home
  - of poverty if the breadwinner is stricken
- loss - of partner and possibly sexual activity
- sadness - due to loss of past times, a sense of bereavement.

Where there has been a close relationship the partner will be apprehensive. The smallest niggles will become gigantic obstacles until everything settles with the support from family, care managers and nursing home staff.

Admitting a married couple

A care manager may consider admitting both husband and wife if:

1. both are in need of care
2. there is suitable accommodation available in the chosen home
3. the home is registered to care for both partners who may have different types of illness, for example, where the wife has had a stroke and the husband suffers from Alzheimer's disease.

Understanding the sick partner

The sick person will also feel guilty about leaving their partner, children, pets and their home.

Before and during the first few days after admission they will feel apprehension. They may worry about:

- their family and how they are coping
- whether they have enough food and whether they are eating
- money or lack of it, if they are the breadwinner
- privacy in their new surroundings
- asking for the toilet and hygiene arrangements
- food, if they will like it or if they can have a choice
- change of doctor and/or medication.

There will be packing to be done and the usual dilemma of what to take and what to leave behind. She will fill him with instructions until his head reels. He will never remember and she will never forget.

When he visits she will ask, 'Did you do...?' She will fret about whether he is sleeping, eating, getting to work on time and who he is seeing. It is impossible for her to believe that her beloved partner is as celibate as he makes out.

Sexual needs

Sexual drive is not cut off because someone has been admitted to residential care. This may make them angry, frustrated and irritable. Unfulfilled need can cause either partner to become aggressive to each other until they both dread visiting times. This is only part of the settling-in period when adjustments to both partners' way of life and innermost feelings are taking place.

TALKING TO THE FAMILY

When a member of the family is admitted to a nursing home it provokes different emotions in all the family members.

Family reactions

The fringe members may find it interesting, passing comment something like, 'At least she will have somebody to look after her now'.

Sons and daughters suffer different emotions: the greatest and most common is one of guilt. Commonplace excuses which are all good reasons for not being able to be a carer are, 'I would look after her myself:

- if I had the time
- if I didn't feel so tired

- if I didn't go out to work
- if ...'

'I'm not getting any younger, I'm retired myself you know.' This phrase is becoming more common as people live longer.

Preventing resentment

Resentment is often felt by the son or daughter who has been forced to take on the full burden of care for their elderly parents because they are separated from their siblings by distance or other reasons.

Sometimes there is one person who takes over, making all the decisions, barely consulting the people who are most affected. Where possible, refer to both partners. Take them to see the most suitable homes and allow them to make their own choice.

These and other related matters need to be brought out into the open and discussed by all the family. The son or daughter will need reassuring that sometimes it is much more practical for their elderly relative to receive residential care, if only for a short period (respite care).

Any resentments or bad feelings may fester, causing family rifts if they are not sorted out at the beginning. This will stop the family pooling ideas and thoughts about your elderly relative and may prove to be detrimental to their future happiness.

Effects on the family

When discussing the future of an elderly relative consider their demands when living with the immediate family. Think about the effects it can have on everybody living within the home:

- The wife (carer) can no longer go out with her husband unless she can find a 'sitter'.
- Children have to be quiet because Granny is dozing.
- Children become frustrated and jealous and feel that mummy cares for Granny more than for them.
- Television must not be too loud as it disturbs Granny.
- Television is so loud it wakes the street because Gran can't hear.
- Shopping is a nightmare. Few shops deliver in this supermarket age.

These are just a few of the changes that may take place. Consider also the extra laundry, particularly if they are incontinent, and higher food and heating bills.

Making a hard decision

It is a hard decision for the family to make. Once it has been made many carers put up with hurtful comments made by people who have no idea what caring 24 hours a day, seven days a week, really entails or the strain it can put on family life.

Listening to friends

Friends sometimes know more about a person than their family. They will often be able to tell you about their previous social life and what kind of a person they are.

Local friends know the area and may advise on the suitability of any local homes for your relative.

CHECKLIST

- Have you discussed nursing home care with your relative?
- Has there been a family discussion?
- What are the opinions of their friends?

CASE STUDIES

Mavis and Julia try to talk to Peter

Mavis met Julia at the hospital. They had gone to talk to Peter about his future. Peter seemed well but vague.

'We are worried about you, Dad,' Mavis said gently.

'I'm OK lass,' he replied

'We would like you to be looked after properly until you're really well,' Julia told him.

Peter didn't answer. His eyes had a faraway look. The sisters continued to talk to him about residential care but he didn't respond. Suddenly he started to live in the past, talking to his constant pit companion of 50 years ago, the canary he took to warn him of gas.

Mavis tried to ask him if he understood what they had been speaking about. He ignored them, talking only to friends from his past. She realised that her father's mental state had deteriorated and was saddened that neither Julia nor she had been able to discuss the situation with him.

Alan and Peggy discuss the future

Alan chose a quiet time to talk to his wife. He didn't want Peggy to feel that she wasn't wanted any more or that she was unloved because she couldn't contribute to the running of the household as she used to do.

Quietly and without fuss he discussed the problems with her, how he could no longer care for her because of his work. Peggy knew that the present situation could not continue. It was expensive for one thing and she was frightened to be alone for too long. They decided to ask the children to come home the following weekend and seek their help.

Peggy and Alan shed tears for the breaking up of their home and the changes in their lives. They grieved for each other and for what might have been.

Audrey brings Aunt Connie home

Audrey West went straight to her aunt's home and was disconcerted to find she was out. She was sure the neighbour was going to be with her. The neighbour said that she had left Connie having a siesta while she went out for a few minutes. When she had got back Connie was gone.

'I have pinned her name and address on her dress so she should be alright,' the neighbour told her.

Audrey was becoming agitated when a kindly lady brought Connie back. She was surprised to see how thin her aunt had become since she had last seen her but soon realised that Connie had not been eating properly.

After tea, Audrey suggested to Connie that they should return to England together. To her surprise her aunt agreed. Audrey phoned her husband saying she would stay for a few days, then bring Auntie home. She asked him to phone Social Services to find out how best to help Connie.

Elizabeth talks to Annie

Annie was a little better when Elizabeth, the choir leader, visited. Her medication had been changed and the pain had gone. The nurses had put her in a chair for a short while.

Elizabeth took her courage in her hands. 'How do you feel about some convalescence, Annie?' she asked.

There was silence at first, then, 'What about Kevin and Fred?'

'Fred is being cared for in ward 9, just across the corridor. You can see him later.'

'What's happened to Kevin?' Annie asked anxiously.

'Kevin has been taken to Sunshine House. I went to see him this morning. He's happy there and he's settled down well.'

Elizabeth could see doubts chasing across Annie's face. 'I think you need to be looked after for a bit longer Annie.'

'I suppose so, but I want to go home in time for Christmas.'

That was the first hurdle over, Elizabeth thought.

DISCUSSION POINTS

1. How has the need for a change in living arrangements affected your relative?
2. Will their partner be able to manage alone?
3. If not, what kind of back-up will the remaining partner need?
4. Who will give any necessary back-up?
5. Is it necessary to involve the care manager – has this been done?
6. Is your relative fit enough to be involved in choosing their new home?

3
Visiting Homes

There are three main types of establishment:

1. a complex incorporating dwellings for self-caring persons
2. converted properties
3. purpose-built homes.

LIVING IN A COMPLEX

Some nursing homes are built within a complex which endeavours to provide total care for the newly retired person until they die. Residents can rent, or buy in some places, a warden-controlled dwelling within the complex. They have the independence of their own home plus the advantages of living within a caring environment. Single and double accommodation, which is usually unfurnished, is generally available.

Changing abilities

If your relative's mobility deteriorates so that they need some assistance with washing, dressing or bathing, they can move into the residential part of the complex where they will be given minimum help.

If they become ill and need nursing care, they can be transferred to the nursing home within the complex. The nursing wing caters for residents with short illnesses such as chest infections and longterm conditions such as arthritis. Residents who undergo surgery would also be cared for until they are well enough to return to their normal accommodation.

Advantages

- This type of establishment gives continuity of care in one place.
- These homes are generally purpose-built or skillfully modified.
- Residents can have their own home with help always at hand if needed.

HOMES				
Things to see/ask	1	2	3	4
Bedrooms				
Furniture				
Commode				
En suite				
Lounge				
Quiet room				
Special baths				
Bath hoists				
General hoist				
Wheelchair ramps				
Gardens				
Meal times				
Position of toilets				
Access to rooms				
Lifts to all parts				
Staffing levels				
Registration doc.				
Insurance cert.				
What's included				
Extras				

Fig. 2. A checklist for the potential new home.

- Continuity of care is available from early retirement for life.
- Opportunities exist to make and continue friendships.
- There are more opportunities for socialising.
- Your relative is more likely to find friends of their own age group.

LIVING IN A CONVERTED BUILDING

Many country homes and large houses have been converted into residential or nursing homes. Because some rooms are too small or have difficult wheelchair access they may be used and registered for residential care only. The home will then be registered as a dual purpose home with the rooms specified as suitable for nursing or residential care.

These homes are rarely single storey and need one or more lifts to reach the upper floors. If there is only one staircase there will be an external fire escape. Some of the older buildings have been country mansions and are magnificent. Many are set in superb grounds and have excellent facilities, but this may be reflected in the fees.

Others are more homely, with narrow corridors, and steps leading to more narrow corridors. They are barely suitable for wheelchair-bound residents.

Advantages

- Rooms in older establishments are often larger.
- The setting and outlook can be picturesque.
- The atmosphere sometimes appears to be more homely.
- Although these homes look large they often have fewer rooms.
- These homes generally have character and warmth.

Disadvantages

- Many have narrow long corridors.
- There are usually more stairs and steps in odd places.
- The lift may be old and small or even non-existent.
- Many older properties are like rabbit warrens which might lead to confusion and disorientation until your relative becomes familiar with their new surroundings.

LIVING IN A PURPOSE-BUILT HOME

All plans for new homes are subject to approval by the health authority inspectorate as well as the normal planning regulations and consents. Plans will be modified to take into account the law and also local regulations and requirements. No new nursing home can be registered unless it meets the required standards.

Designing for the resident's needs

Purpose-built nursing homes are designed with the needs of the elderly person in mind. Many of the newer homes are built on a single level. Residents find that this gives them better access to the lounge, their room and toilet facilities. They tend to become more independent and confident.

The well-designed home might include:

- good sized rooms, legal minimum ten square metres (single)
- wide doors and corridors
- large lounge or community room
- separate dining room
- quiet room
- activities room
- sufficient toilet facilities
- hairdressing salon
- treatment room large enough for chiropody/physiotherapy
- plenty of storage space
- matron's and administrator's offices on the ground floor
- nurses' stations on each floor
- handrails
- adequate fire exits as stipulated by the fire officer.

Advantages

- They have easier access to the nursing home facilities.
- Modern baths and equipment will have been installed.

- The rooms and communal areas are generally more spacious.
- The grounds are suitable for elderly people.
- The decor is modern and light.

Disadvantages

- Modern buildings are not liked by some older people.
- If the building is very new, there will be a time of upheaval while the 'snagging' (repairing of plaster cracks that appear whilst the building is drying out) programme is carried out.

SEEING THE MATRON

If you have made an appointment it is always helpful if you can be on time. Sometimes other appointments have been made to fit into a busy schedule.

Taking a list

Take with you a list of the initial queries you have. Note the answers. A 'tick' list is useful as it involves little writing during your visit. Remember particularly to check:

- the fees and extras
- visiting times
- capability to cope with your relative.

Remember this is your initial visit – ask only basic questions at this time. Gain more complicated information on your second visit.

Questions you may be asked

Matron will verify your relative's details, needs, personal preferences and type of room required. You will be asked about their illness or disabilities, their weight and general build, known allergies, medicines they are currently taking and their mental state.

Making her own assessment

Matron may wish to visit your relative at home or in hospital to make her own assessment before she will agree to admit them. This is not usually done until you have decided that this is the home of choice.

INSPECTING THE PREMISES

Have your checklist in your hand and tick off each item as you see it, making notes as you go along.

Places you should see

- Bedrooms ____
- Lifts - that they go to all floors ____
- Lounge ____
- Dining room ____
- Bathroom and toilets ____
- Quiet room ____
- Kitchen/s from the doorway ____
- Gardens ____

Looking at bedrooms

- Is the room large enough? ____
- Are the door and windows easy to open and close? ____
- Does the sun come in the morning or afternoon? ____
- Is the outlook uplifting, stimulating or depressing? ____
- Is the room single or shared? ____
- If shared, ask about the other occupant. ____
- Is the bed comfortable? ____
- Is the bed linen adequate and clean? ____
- Are personal televisions supplied? ____

Fixtures and fittings should include

- A wash hand basin ____
- Soap and paper towel dispenser ____
- Mirror ____

En suite facilities include

- Toilet ____
- Possibly a bath or shower unit ____

Furnishings, furniture and decor

- Furnishings are usually simple. ____
- The walls may be papered or painted. ____
- Bedspreads and curtains are sometimes colour co-ordinated. ____
- Is there carpet or lino on the floor? ____
- Are rugs and mats securely fixed? ____

Furniture should include

Bed ____
Bedside cabinet ____
Wardrobe and chest of drawers or a combined unit ____
Commode (if required) ____
One armchair and one chair for visitors ____
Private lockable facility for the resident's use ____
Privacy curtains or screens in shared rooms ____
Adjustable over-bed table ____

Most homes allow residents to bring either some or all of their own furniture but:

- It must be free from woodworm and other diseases.
- It must be safe – all upholstery must be fire retardant.
- Wardrobes may have to be fixed to the wall to prevent them toppling.
- Furniture must be small enough to fit into the room comfortably.

Personal electrical items

Please note: all electrical items, television sets, electrically operated beds *etc* that you take in for your relative must have a safety check by an electrician.

Sitting in the lounge

Some homes have a lounge/diner; others have two separate rooms.

Is there enough space for the residents? ____
Are the chairs comfortable? ____
Are the residents seated so they can communicate with each other? ____
Check noise levels from television and radios. ____
Is there enough table room for all? ____
Is the carpet clean? ____

Depending on the time you visit you may see several residents sitting in the lounge. Look at them, speak to them. Remember some may be deaf or unable to communicate and will not respond.

Do they appear happy and content? ____
Do they look clean and well cared for? ____

Do they say good things about the home? ____

Bathrooms and toilets

Do you think there are sufficient facilities for the number of residents? ____
Are the toilets clean and tidy? ____
Do they smell fresh? ____
Are there any specially designed baths like the Parker Bath? ____
Are there hoists for the heavier resident? ____
Are there grab rails and toilet aids? ____

Linen

Note the linen, whether it is clean and in good repair. Ask how often bed linen, towels, tablecloths and personal clothing are changed and laundered.

Kitchen/s

Owing to health and environmental regulations you will not be able to enter the kitchen. However, you can see, smell and hear from the doorway.

A busy kitchen is not always tidy but is it clean? ____
Do the kitchen staff have clean uniforms, aprons and hats? ____
Does the kitchen equipment look clean? ____
Does the crockery and cutlery look clean? ____
Is the smell of cooking appetising? ____

Walking in the grounds

Gardens can be a great source of pleasure to residents and their relatives. If the grounds are suitable a resident can either walk or be wheeled out into the garden.

- Fresh air is a great morale booster.
- Bird song and garden scents can delight the blind person.
- Colour and the feel of a breeze can be enjoyed by the deaf.

Looking at the garden

Is the garden suitable? ____
Are there seats available? ____

Is it likely to catch the sun most of the day? ____
Is there a summer house or similar? ____
Are there any raised gardens for the residents? ____
Is there easy access to all parts of the garden? ____
Is there a safe patio? ____

Although many people enjoy being outside, bear in mind that there are some who either can't go outside or dislike the great outdoors. This may be due to hay fever and allergies, agoraphobia or other illnesses.

CHECKLIST

- Make sure you see everything you need to see.
- Don't forget to write your comments on your checklist.
- Check what furniture or other items can be taken in.

CASE STUDIES

Mavis finds the right home for Peter

Although Peter's physical health has improved, his mental health has deteriorated. He is unaware of his surroundings, is aggressive at times and does not recognise his daughters.

Mavis and Julia discussed Peter's physical and mental health with the doctor, ward sister and his care manager. It was decided that Mavis should look for an EMI home (home catering for elderly mentally ill residents).

Peter's care manager gave Mavis a list of homes, pointing out which ones were registered to care for residents like Peter.

Mavis phoned the homes for information, which arrived within two days. Of the four homes lying within reasonable distance she made appointments to visit two. Before she visited the homes, Ashcroft House and Virginia Lodge, she drew up a list of things she wanted to see and ask.

Whilst she looked around she tried to experience what her father would feel if he lived there. Virginia Lodge was modern and large with big airy rooms. Ashcroft House was a converted manor house catering for 24 residents. It's decor was not as modern but the rooms were nicely appointed. When Mavis walked in she felt a serenity and happiness. Father would like it here, she thought.

Alan looks around

Alan went to the care manager's clinic at the doctor's surgery to discuss the problems Peggy and he were experiencing. The care manager was already aware of the situation and was relieved that they had come to this decision. He gave Alan a list of registered homes and suggested that he get back in touch when he had found somewhere suitable.

Alan and Peggy went through the list, crossing off the ones that were too far away or where access would be difficult if the car broke down. There were still about 20 left. Alan looked in *Yellow Pages* for any information that would help them to whittle down the list. Another ten homes were discarded in this way.

Because Alan was not at home during office hours he wrote to the remaining homes for brochures and information. Peggy and Alan spent the weekend sorting through the brochures and short-listed four that he would visit. He asked a neighbour to ring for appointments on the following Friday when he had an annual leave day due.

Although Peggy wanted him to make a list of everything Alan preferred to trust his memory.

Alan left the house at nine o'clock, returning at lunch-time. He had made some notes but had forgotten much of what he wanted to ask or see. As he had still another two homes to visit in the afternoon he decided he would make a list after all.

The afternoon visits over, Alan returned home exhausted. 'I never realised how tiring it would be looking at nursing homes,' he told his wife.

Connie is assessed

Audrey finally managed to get Aunt Connie home. She put up a bed for her in the dining room as a temporary measure. The next day Connie fell and appeared to be in some discomfort with her left ankle. The doctor visited and after he had examined Connie, Audrey asked how she could be helped.

The doctor said he would send Connie for an X-ray and refer her to the consultant geriatrician and social services.

Connie had a severe sprain and was suffering from bruising and shock. The doctor in the accident and emergency department decided to admit her for a few days. During this time she was seen by the consultant, who kept her in for assessment and physiotherapy.

A few weeks later Audrey was told that she would need to find a residential home for Connie as she had not responded to rehabilitation and needed constant supervision.

Audrey had already sent for brochures, made her checklists and visited some of the homes in the locality.

Elizabeth looks for a double room

Although Annie had said she wanted to return home, Elizabeth knew that she would fret much less if Fred could be with her during her convalescence. She also thought that Annie would stay longer and maybe permanently. She talked the whole thing over with the pastor and senior church members. All were in agreement.

There was no immediate shortage of money, but what they had would last them only three months. In view of the fact that the money would soon run out it was decided that their care manager should be involved.

The pastor had visited church members in the Devonshire Complex on many occasions and he had been impressed with the buildings, standards of care and the contentment of both residents and staff. Elizabeth thought she would visit and see for herself what was on offer. She phoned for an appointment to see the matron and the home.

Elizabeth was impressed. Everybody was polite and kind. The staff looked happy and bright. Her appointment was at lunch time and the delicious smell and sight of food greeted her as she passed the dining room on her tour of the home.

There were three main parts to the complex:

1. A terrace of ten bungalows set in their own gardens, each containing a double bedroom, lounge, kitchen and shower room. All the rooms had fitted cupboards and the kitchen had room for a washing machine. Laundry could be done by the laundry staff if preferred. The rent was a little higher than expected but it did include all electricity, hot water, heating and laundry if required. It also had the advantage of a call system and a daily visit from one of the trained nurses.

2. A residential home catering for 35 residents on two floors.

3. A 40-bed nursing home.

All buildings had single and double rooms and the complex was ideal for Annie and Fred. Elizabeth picked up brochures and leaflets and made notes of everything she saw to take back to Annie and Fred.

DISCUSSION POINTS

1. Does your relative need a nursing or residential home?
2. Compare the different homes you have seen.
3. Is the home you find most appealing the best one for your relative?
4. Would your relative prefer a shared or a single room?
5. Are *en suite* facilities a necessity?

4
Assessing the Information

Not all areas have the same number of homes catering for elderly people. For instance, Tunbridge Wells has about 40 homes, whereas the Isle of Sheppey has only one nursing home plus a handful of residential homes. You may consider looking in a nearby town or place that is easily accessible if there is nothing suitable in your preferred locality.

If you are living in a place surrounded by residential and nursing homes you will be spoilt for choice and possibly confused.

You will have a stack of brochures and information awaiting your attention. By now you will have visited most of the homes you are interested in and already have some completed checklists.

STUDYING THE BROCHURES

- Look at the literature and your completed checklists.
- Divide it into piles: – instant appeal
  – possible
  – unsuitable.

Remember:

- Photographs can be misleading: rooms may look more spacious than they are in reality.
- Brochures are a commercial advertisement and are not always representative of the home.
- Brochures may be out of date.
- Practices may have changed since the brochure was published.
- The home may have new owners and/or new management with different ideas.

Scanning the homes with instant appeal

- Are any of them in the right area?
- Note down what you like about them.
- Do the listed facilities meet your relative's requirements?
- Shortlist the homes that appear to be most suitable.
- If you haven't already visited, phone for an appointment to view.
- Ask for directions if necessary.

Note how the phone is answered. Is the person you spoke to interested? Their manner might be indicative of the general attitude of the staff.

Avoiding information overload

It is unwise to visit more than three or four homes in a day because:

- it's exhausting, mentally and physically
- it's difficult to remember, even with a checklist, what you've seen
- absorbing the atmosphere of each home becomes impossible if you have not allowed sufficient time.

PAYING A SECOND VISIT

If you decide to make a second visit it may be possible to take your relative with you. If not you should try to discuss the options with them. This helps them feel they have a choice – and a hand in the management of their future.

Make out a new checklist with all the things listed that you didn't ask before. Add everything you've thought of since that first visit. See the suggested list in Figure 3. Customise it to suit the circumstances.

- Allow plenty of time for the second visit.
- Take your relative if possible.
- Ask another family member or friend to go with you.
- Make sure you ask all the questions you want answers to.
- Ask to see the report of the last health authority inspection. (When health authority inspectors make a full inspection a report is always

HOMES				
What to see/ask	1	2	3	4
Bedroom again				
Menus				
Activities programme				
Library				
Alcoholic drinks				
Smoking allowed?				
Pocket money				
Outings				
Hairdressing				
Chiropody				
Physiotherapy				
Visiting				
Own furniture?				
Church activities				
Television				
Radio				
Personal insurance				
Registered for?				
Post/letters				
Pets				
Newspapers				

Fig. 3. A checklist for the second visit.

sent to the home. Proprietors, managers and matrons are expected to read it and make any necessary improvements that have been recommended).

- Don't be fobbed off with vague responses.
- Use all your senses. Listen to what they tell you.
- Don't commit yourself or your relative to anything unless you are absolutely sure.
- Ask if they could be admitted for a trial period.

Remember: Proprietors and senior staff will welcome your questions if they care for your relative's wellbeing.

LOOKING FOR QUALITY

The Nursing Home Charter

Some health authorities have drawn up a charter which sets out the rights, responsibilities, risks and restrictions that affect residents in care homes. It is designed to inform residents living in nursing homes exactly what they are entitled to (see Figure 4). Unfortunately, this is

NURSING HOME CHARTER

Entitlements

As a resident living in a Nursing Home you should have the same rights and freedom as any other person living in the community.

Accountability

Your personal actions have consequences which may affect other residents, visitors or staff. Nobody has complete freedom to do as they please. A Nursing Home is no different in this respect.

Adverse Consequences

Residents living in nursing homes are encouraged to be as independent as their particular circumstances permit. Independence brings its own risks particularly if you are already affected by age, illness or disability. Everybody lives with a certain amount of risk which is considered normal. It would be wrong to limit your freedom just because you are a resident in a nursing home.

Fig. 4. Nursing Home Charter.

CLOISTERS NURSING HOME

We commit all persons working in and associated with the home to enable you, as a resident in the Cloisters Nursing Home, to enjoy the following rights.

The following are your rights

To be treated as an individual.

To have your personal dignity respected.

Privacy for yourself and your affairs.

To have your cultural, religious and emotional needs accepted and respected.

To develop and maintain social contacts and interests.

To participate in regular reviews of your individual circumstances, and to have an adviser present if you so wish.

To undertake for yourself the tasks of daily living which you are able to do.

Personal independence, choice and responsibility for your actions.

To have the same access to facilities and services in the community as any other citizen.

To manage your own financial affairs or to be able to lawfully delegate that authority to another person who will act on your behalf and carry out your wishes.

To be consulted about your medical treatment and medication.

To receive care planned by a first level nurse and to participate as fully as possible in planning your own individual care.

To be represented by an advocate.

To have access to your own personal file.

To be informed of a formal complaints procedure and to be represented by a friend or adviser if you so wish.

Fig. 5. Example of a resident's charter.

not a universal charter but the same rights apply to everybody whether a charter has been drawn up or not.

Management teams that adhere to the principles of such a charter automatically provide residents with a feeling that they are still human beings; that their feelings and dignity are respected and that they are still important members of the community.

A charter does not necessarily have to be drawn up and issued by a health authority. Many homes have their own charter and philosophy of care (see the example in Figure 5). Some will argue that a document of this kind is unnecessary. However, if residents and staff are aware of the contents of a charter it will result in better training, ongoing care, attitudes and respect.

Staff training

All staff need periods of training. These can range from basic instruction for the novice, to advanced seminars for trained staff.

The tuition and education of student nurses and care assistants have changed in recent years. Trained staff must now prove that they are receiving regular post-basic education either by private study or by attending formal lectures and/or courses.

Care assistants have the opportunity to work for their NVQs (National Vocational Qualifications) in addition to in-house training. These courses teach basic to advanced levels of care and are run in conjunction with the practical skills they learn in their workplace.

Weekly activities

Many homes run weekly activities for the residents (see Figure 6). This offers them enjoyment and stimulation. The programme is usually changed each week, and the most popular occupation seems to be prize bingo. The prizes are small, such as a bar of chocolate or a tablet of soap, but that doesn't detract from the pleasure it gives. Other activities that give residents pleasure are painting, crafts, sing songs and creating Christmas decorations. If your relative has a favourite pastime it could be incorporated into the programme if you mention it to matron.

Quality assurance

During the last few years great emphasis has been laid on quality assurance in services and business. Many firms insist that their staff participate in training and controlled routines in order to obtain the coveted quality standard ISO 9000 (formerly BS 5750).

Some nursing homes have worked for and achieved the required standards that have led to the presentation of the award.

Working towards the award

It can take from six months to a year or longer to reach the standards set by the examiners. Every aspect of care is taken into consideration and examined, including procedures, catering, cleanliness, staff attitudes, training and grooming. It requires 100 per cent commitment of all personnel to achieve the required standards.

Maintenance of standards

Maintaining the set standards of the home is an ongoing exercise. All new members of staff have to be trained to work to the high standard already obtained.

Day	Morning	Afternoon
Monday	Interdenominational Church service	Crafts Audio tapes
Tuesday	Individual dressing practice	Music and movement
Wednesday	Hairdressing	Birthday party
Thursday	Nail care	Sing song Prize bingo
Friday	Individual dressing practice	Cards Board games
Saturday	Coffee morning	Video film
Sunday	Television/radio Church service for people who wish	Afternoon tea with visitors
Check with the doctor that there are no medical reasons to prevent a resident participating in the music and movement class before allowing them to join in.		

Fig.6. Programme of weekly activities.

In order to ensure that the home remains worthy of the award an examining procedure is periodically carried out. If standards slip, further training is required. The award is withdrawn until the examiners are satisfied that the home is worthy of it again.

Educating staff in good practices

The Nursing Home Charter, in-house training, NVQs and quality assurance awards can only be good tools for promoting excellent care for residents:

Ask matron:

- Whether staff training is encouraged?
- What kind of staff training takes place within the home?
- Are any staff studying for their NVQ?

CHECKLIST

- Did you fill in a checklist?
- If you didn't like the homes you visited, have you made appointments to view others?
- Have you taken time to consider the merits, or otherwise, of the homes you have visited?
- Are you and your relative happy with your choice of home? If not start again!

CASE STUDIES

Mavis and Julia decide on the Ashcroft Nursing Home

Mavis and Julia visited the Ashcroft Nursing Home for the second time. While they were waiting for matron to come Julia noticed the registration and insurance certificates hanging on the wall. She noted that the home was registered to care for the Elderly Mentally Ill person.

As Peter was incapable of appreciating the visit they had left him on the ward. Julia liked the nursing home and felt, as Mavis did, that the homely environment and caring staff would benefit him.

They asked if there was still a bed available. Matron showed them

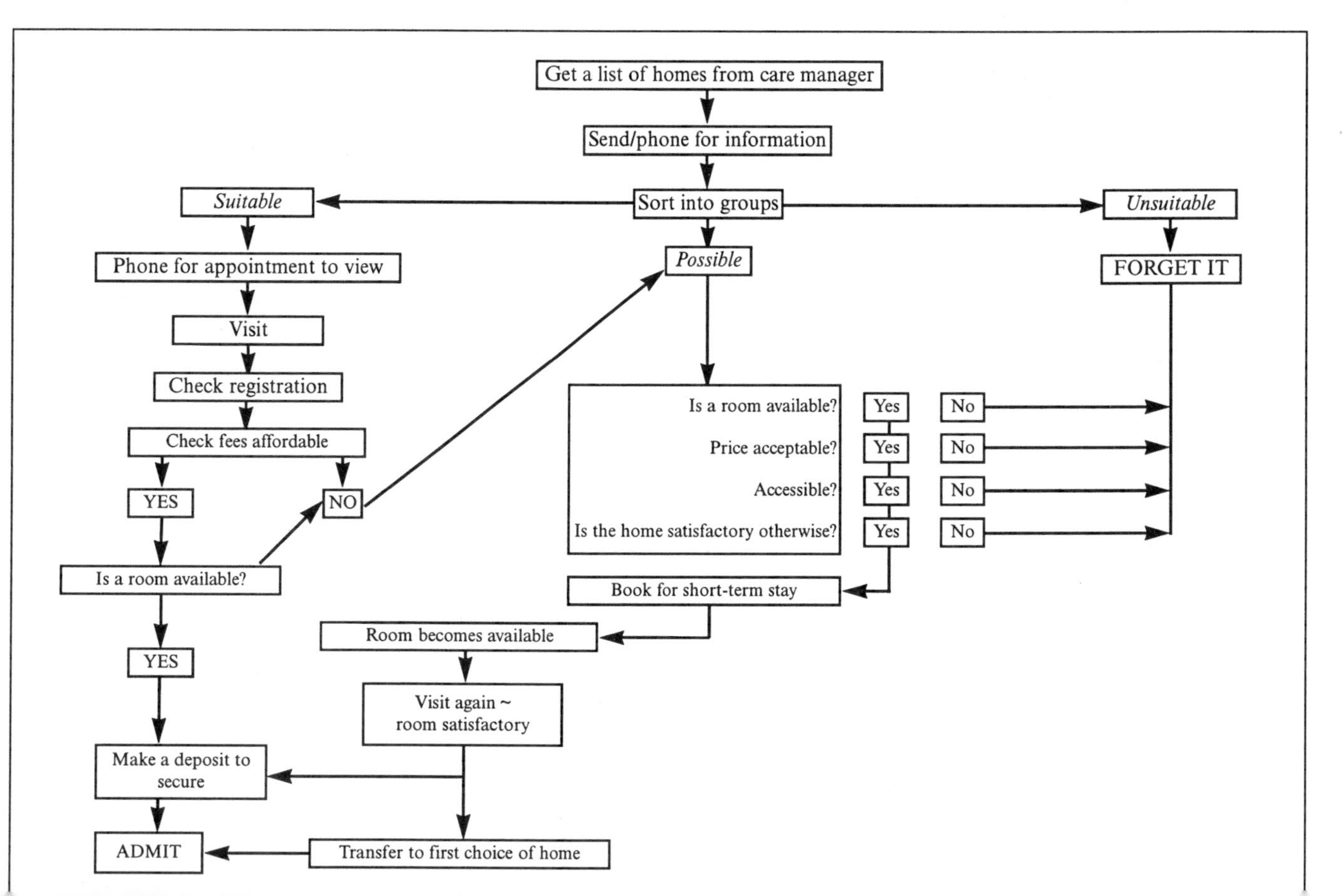

Fig. 7. Sorting the information.

the available rooms but told them she would visit and assess him before contacting his care manager to arrange his admission.

Peggy is taken to see two homes

Alan arranged for Peggy to be taken to two homes by private ambulance. It was costly but Alan wanted her to make her own choice. Both matrons and their staff welcomed her but Peggy liked the Brambles Nursing Home best.

It was a purpose-built single-storey building incorporating bedrooms, dining rooms and leisure areas. There were several bathrooms all fitted with special baths or hoists. Toilets had grab rails and some had raised seats. The corridors were spacious enough for her wheelchair and there was ample space to get her large bed into her room through the wide double doors.

Peggy asked if she could stay for a trial period for a few days. Matron agreed but advised against her bringing her special bed in until she was sure she wanted to stay.

Matron said they would put a Spenco Mattress on her bed as a temporary measure. It was agreed that Peggy would be admitted in three days' time. Alan said he would pack a few things that Peggy would need for her temporary stay. He asked if he could bring in Peggy's television. When matron informed him electrical items had to be checked he said he would take it to an electrician and get it tested.

Audrey looks at Cloisters Manor

Connie's general health had improved since having regular meals and a more ordered routine in the hospital. She no longer seemed to have the urge to wander off alone and appeared quite content to sit and talk or watch television. Sometimes she played patience and her niece remembered that Connie always used to enjoy a game of whist or bridge. Audrey wondered whether her aunt would be quite so content if she were left to her own devices for very long.

A care manager visited to discuss the way forward. After talking to both Connie and Audrey she suggested that Connie might be happiest in a residential home. She gave Audrey a list of homes indicating the type of homes they were. Audrey was told that in view of her aunt's wealth she need not involve social services. However, if help or advice was needed she could contact the care manager who would try and sort out any problems.

REGISTERED HOMES ACT 1984

Certificate of Registration

THIS IS TO CERTIFY that Mr A N Other

of 63 Central Avenue, Gatespear, Nomansland X12 Y12

carrying on a Nursing Home at 63 Nonsuch Road, Nonsuch Town, Nomansland X12 Z21 known as "The Ashcroft Nursing Home"

has been registered in respect of such home by Nomansland Health Authority

under the provisions of the Registered Homes Act 1984 xxxx xxxxxxxxxxxxxxxxxxxxxxxxxxxxxxxxxxxxxxxxxxxxxxxxxxxxxxx xxxxxxxxxxxxxxxxxxxxxxx

CONDITIONS OF REGISTRATION:

1. The number of persons for whom accommodation is provided at any one time shall not exceed 30 (Thirty).

*

2. That patients detained under the Mental Health Act (1993) will not be accepted.

(*Insert any other condition(s) imposed under s. 29 of the Act)
Delete words in square brackets if they do not apply.

Signed...

on behalf of the registration authority

Dated...........24 MAY 19xx....
No..............................

THIS CERTIFICATE MUST BE DISPLAYED CONSPICUOUSLY IN THE HOME - FAILURE TO DO SO IS AN OFFENCE.

Fig. 8. A sample registration certificate.

The third home that Audrey visited seemed ideal. It was dual registered and was constructed in the shape of a square. Four wings surrounded a covered walkway with arches leading into a well established garden with seats, a bird bath and pathways.

The rooms were bright, most had a door opening out on to the walkway with ramps for wheelchairs. Audrey decided to take all the information back to Connie: if she liked the look of Cloisters Audrey would bring her to see it for herself.

Annie and Fred decide to go to the Devonshire complex

Annie liked the photographs and what Elizabeth told her about the Devonshire complex. As soon as she was well enough Elizabeth took her and Fred to see it. Matron showed them over the bungalows, the residential part and the nursing home.

During this time matron quietly assessed them. She had already telephoned the hospital to establish their state of health, and felt that they were not well enough to live in the bungalow. In view of Annie's health and Fred's recent surgery and prognosis she thought they should be cared for in the nursing home section. Annie was rather disappointed but cheered up when she was shown a spacious ground-floor double room.

Annie asked if they could still join in the activities of the complex. They were reassured that they could, providing they were well enough at the time.

They both liked the home and decided that they would pay a deposit of £50 to hold the room until they could take up residence.

Elizabeth informed the hospital and the care manager of their decision.

DISCUSSION POINTS

1. Do you think that having a charter will make any difference to the way a home is run?

2. Quality assurance – does it affect the fees?

3. What 'extras' are needed?

5
Paying the Bills

COMPARING FEES

Every home has its own fee structure. Most charge different amounts for single and shared rooms. Some charge more for highly dependent residents. Others require a basic fee but charge extra for everything other than basic care, even for giving a visitor a cup of tea.

Residents who pay for themselves (self-funding) are often charged higher fees than residents who are funded by the local authority.

Because most people forget the facts and figures that they most want to remember, it is a good idea to visit each home with a list of questions you need to ask. Leave enough space on the paper to jot down the answers.

Ask for a list of fees and an explanation of the fee structure and 'extras' that need to be taken into account.

UNDERSTANDING BASIC FEES

Few homes charge an all-inclusive fee these days, although most homes include incontinence aids in their price. Normally the fees include: nursing care, bed linen, food, special diets, use of equipment, domestic services and laundering of all home linen.

Additional charges

Residents may be expected to pay for everything other than basic care. Some of the items listed below may incur extra costs:

- hiring of equipment: for example, special beds (Mediscus)
- residents who are heavily dependent
- extra staff for nursing on a one-to-one basis (specialling)

- incontinence pads and pants
- personal laundry and dry cleaning
- visitors' refreshments and meals
- occupational therapy materials
- outings
- speech therapy
- physiotherapy
- hairdressing
- chiropody
- alcoholic drinks
- private consultants' and doctors' visits
- private prescriptions
- anything else the management feels isn't covered by the basic fees.

Find out what is included and what is termed as an extra.

Room fees

Basic fees can be as low as £300.00 per week for a place in a shared room. Health authority inspectors agree that no more than two people should share and that they should be of the same sex unless they are a married couple.

Additions to the basic fee

Higher fees are generally charged for:

- large single rooms
- normal size single rooms
- double rooms used as single
- *en suite* facilities (may be a bathroom or a toilet and hand basin).

A fee list might look like the example on page 58.

ASHCROFT NURSING HOME List of fees		
Facility	*Daily fee* £ p	*Weekly fee* £ p
Large single room	54.00	378.00
Large single with *en suite*	57.00	399.00
Small single	52.00	364.00
Small single with *en suite*	54.00	378.00
Double room used as single	87.00	609.00
Shared room per resident	47.00	329.00

Absences (for example, holidays or hospitalisation):

– Less than seven days no reduction.

– More than seven days ten per cent reduction.

– Short-term rates (less than one calendar month) £60.00 per day.

Absence from the home

Residents are sometimes admitted into hospital or leave the home to go on holiday for a week or two. If you wish to take them away for any period of time inform the matron as soon as possible. Any discounts that become due will be shown on the appropriate invoices.

You can, of course, relinquish the room if your relative is going on a prolonged absence. However, if they wish to return they may find that 'their' room has been filled or that the terms and conditions of admission have changed. Fee increases can be brought forward a month or two for new admissions.

Discounts for absence

Discounts are not usually given for an absence of seven days or less. Depending on the policy of the home a discount of ten per cent may be allowed for periods of longer than one week. Check your relative's contract or with the matron.

Increasing the fees

If your relative is self-funding ask the matron how frequently the fees are reviewed. It will probably be in April of each year or six monthly. Projected fee increases are usually decided on at the annual audit but may be slightly adjusted during the year depending on increasing prices of commodities.

For example: it may have been decided to raise the fees by seven per cent at the beginning of the home's financial year. Due to increasing food prices and rising costs of disposables a further fee increase of two per cent may be introduced half way through the year.

Matron may be able to inform you of any impending increases and how much the fees are likely to rise in the forthcoming year. Take account of them in your budget.

- The frequency of fee increases should be stated in your relative's contract.
- One month's notice of impending fee increases is generally given.

Making a deposit

Once you have decided on the room in a home and agreed the fees you may be asked for a non-returnable deposit.

- It's payable from the moment the bed/room is reserved.
- Some homes ask for £100.00; others ask for one week's fee.
- If, after paying a deposit, your relative decides not to stay at the home the deposit is forfeited.

Short-term stays (respite care)

If your relative is self-funding and being admitted for one month or less they will probably be asked to pay the whole of the basic fees in advance. They will also be expected to settle any 'extras' before their discharge.

If your relative is being funded by the local authority the style of the invoice will depend on which method the local authority uses to pay for the care your relative receives. For instance, if the fees are paid to the home, the invoice will be for extras only. If, however, the money is paid to your relative for them to pay to the home, they will be invoiced for their fees plus any extras.

- Make sure that your relative wants/needs to go into residential care.
- Make the right choice before paying a deposit.
- Remember that in most cases the deposit is non-returnable.

Death before admission

If your relative dies before reaching the home, inform the matron immediately and ask for a refund. It may or may not be granted depending on the policy of the home.

Receiving the invoice

If your relative is self-funding they will receive invoices either every four weeks or every calendar month in advance. Accounts are expected to be settled promptly.

In addition to the basic fee your relative will be billed for any extras, such as hairdressing and chiropody.

The first invoice will show the basic fee plus any extras minus any deposit paid.

Settling the account

All businesses rely on prompt payment. Care homes are no exception.

Should there be a delay in settling the account within a given time limit you may be charged interest on the unpaid amount.

CALCULATING FEES

Four weekly accounts

Four weekly fee totals are calculated by multiplying the weekly amount, say £325.00, by four, making a total of £1,300.

Calendar monthly fees are calculated as follows:

Multiply the weekly fee, say £325.00, by 52 and divide by 12.

Therefore:

£325.00 × 52 = £16,900 (annual total) ÷ 12 = £1,408.33 (monthly total).

Daily fees

Daily fees are calculated either by the day or by the night, depending on the home. The amount is calculated by dividing the weekly fee by seven. Therefore:

£325.00 ÷ 7 = £46.43 per day (night).

GETTING FINANCIAL SUPPORT

Your relative's future home has been chosen. The care manager has been informed.

Assuming that income support will be required either now or in the future, a financial assessment will be made by social services at the time when the support is needed. For instance, if it is needed immediately, the financial assessment will be carried out before they are admitted. However, if financial support isn't needed until your relative's money runs out, say in three years' time, the assessment will be made when their capital drops to £16,000. (At the time of writing this is the threshold to qualify for income support.)

The interview

Your relative is at liberty to ask a relative, friend or yourself to be with them during the interview. Sometimes power of attorney is given to an appointed person who undertakes to look after their affairs and well-being. This could be you!

Assessing the relative's income

Your elderly relative may not like discussing their personal wealth, or lack of it, with a stranger. They may feel it's degrading and a breach of privacy. Personal finances are still taboo with most people when it comes to discussion. Anybody attempting to interfere is regarded as prying and your relative may become agitated or angry during and after the interview.

Approaching the subject of finances

Your relative's care manager will probably conduct the interview. Care managers are trained to approach delicate matters sensitively and sympathetically without causing their clients distress. They are aware that many elderly people feel that asking for financial help is begging and receiving it is charity. This is against their principles.

It's a hangover from pre-war days when everybody was brought up to believe that to accept any form of hand-out was a disgrace. Starving, homeless or sick people would only apply for 'National Assistance' as a last resort.

Times have changed. Now the onus of care is upon the social services.

Your relative's financial assessment

Before an application for income support can be made the care manager has to make an assessment of your relative's financial needs.

Your relative or their representative (this may be you) will be asked for details of:

- source of income

The Brambles Nursing Home
34 Nonsuch Place
Nonsuch Town
Tel: 0000 0000

1 August 19xx

Mr Alan Bright
13 Brighton Avenue
Nonsuch Town

Ref.No. 23/7/01

Fees in respect of nursing care for Mrs Bright

	£ p
Fees from 23-31 July 19xx	417.85
Fees from 1-31 August 19xx	1,408.33
	1,826.18
Deposit paid 1 July 19xx	100.00
Total:	£1,726.18

The Company reserve the right to charge interest at 3% above base rates if the account is not settled by 20 August 19xx.

Fig. 9. Sample invoices.

Cloisters Nursing Home
14 Nonsuch Gardens
Nonsuch Town
Tel: 0000 0000

2 September 19xx

Mrs Audrey West
46 Nonsuch Road
Nonsuch Town

Ref.No. 23/7/02

Fees in respect of Miss Connie Crisp

		£ p	£ p
Fees from 1/10/19xx - 31/10/xx			1,408.33
Hairdressing			
2/9/xx	Perm	10.00	
7/9/xx	Shampoo & set	4.00	
12/9/xx	" " "	4.00	
19/9/xx	" " "	4.00	
26/9/xx	" " "	4.00	
	Total:	£26.00	£26.00
Newspapers/magazines at £3.00 weekly			£12.00
		Total:	£1,446.33

Interest will be charged at 2% above base rate on all accounts not settled before 12 October 19xx.

Fig. 9. Sample invoices – continued.

- pensions, private and state
- income support and any allowances
- any other income they currently receive.

The amount of financial help they will be eligible for will depend on:

- their total income
- their savings
- property or other assets they might own.

At the present time a person who has savings of more than:

- £16,000 is not eligible to receive income support;
- £10,000 but less than £16,000 can receive help on a sliding scale.

Maximum financial help is given to people with less than £10,000.

Claiming income support (residential allowance)

When the care manager has obtained the necessary information they will help you to apply for any income support (residential allowance) that your relative is eligible for.

Taking financial advice

There are financial advisers who are only too willing to take money for giving advice. Many people who accept such offers pay dearly for guidance which is totally unsuitable for their circumstances. If you are worried about your relative's finances ask their bank manager or somebody else who is knowledgeable and trustworthy for advice.

AGREEING THE FEES

If your relative is not seeking financial help from the social services the weekly/monthly fees will be agreed with the matron. She will suggest ways to pay the account as it becomes due. Choose the method which is easiest for them or their representative.

Ways of paying

Check with the matron which method of payment is acceptable. There are three primary options:

1. By **direct debit.** This is easiest. Matron will give you the appropriate form to complete which your relative can sign before it is sent to their bank. Payments to the home are then made automatically from their account. Payments can be of a fixed sum covering the basic fees only or of a variable amount to cover extras and any fee increases.
2. By sending a monthly or weekly **cheque**.
3. By paying **cash**. The old DSS allowances are still payable at post offices. Some people prefer to draw this money for their relative, then take the cash to the home. This is not the best method. Large sums of money can get lost or stolen.

- **Credit cards** are not generally accepted in nursing homes.
- Always ask for a **receipt** particularly when paying cash.

MAKING UP THE ALLOWANCES

Income support (see Figure 10) is composed of two parts:

The residential allowance

Your relative will be eligible for this allowance if they are claiming income support towards the cost of their residential or nursing home.

Social services allow a personal allowance of up to £56.50 plus a residential allowance of £51.00 each week. The residential allowance may be increased if you live in Greater London.

Your relative's total income will be taken into account before these allowances can be made. If their income is below the allowances, they will get the balance between their income and the allowances.

Example

Personal allowance	£56.50
Residential allowance	£51.00
	£107.50
minus Mrs Smith's weekly income	£60.00
Mrs Smith will get an allowance of	£47.50

The cheque for this allowance will be sent to your relative on a regular basis.

Payment by the local authority

The remainder of the income support will be paid by the local authority, either direct to the nursing home or to your relative.

Payment to your relative

Local authorities have various methods of making payments. Some make payment to the resident. The resident then uses the money towards their fees.

Example

Mrs Smith is eligible to receive £200.00 per week towards the nursing home fees of £320.00. She will receive:

Residential allowance:	£190.00 in every four weekly period
Income support:	£610.00 in every four weekly period
Total:	£800.00

Mrs Smith would then have to add another £480.00 making the total £1,280.00 to pay the full cost of her fees.

Payment to the home

Some local authorities pay direct to the home and then send a bill to the resident for any money they pay to the home which is over and above the agreed allowance.

For example: Peggy Bright has been allowed £300.00 per week towards the contracted price of £320.00 per week of a bed at the Brambles. The local authority pay the Brambles £1,280.00 every four weeks. They also send a bill to Peggy for £80.00 every four weeks. This is the amount of money they have paid to the home in excess of what Peggy is eligible for. She would then need to send a cheque for £80.00 to the local authority.

Ask your relative's care manager to explain the procedure more fully to you.

Protected DSS payments

Up until 31 March 1993 any person requiring nursing home or residential care could be referred to a home by a doctor, social worker, hospital or relative. They would apply for the appropriate DSS allowance (income support).

Providing the application was approved, the DSS allowance could be collected from the post office on a weekly basis. This money was then used to pay the home fees.

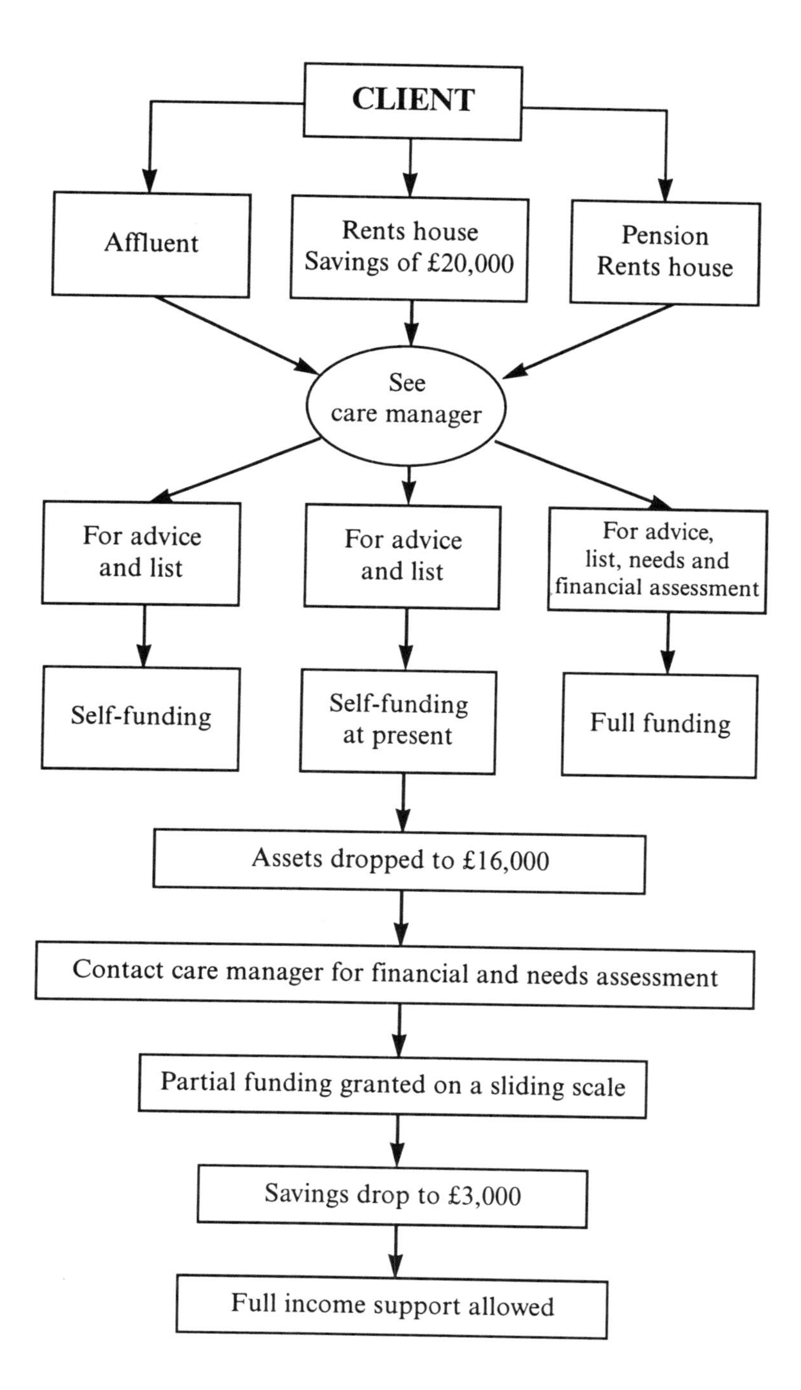

Fig. 10. Qualifying for income support.

Residential fees were, and still are, lower than nursing home fees but a resident needing nursing care could be transferred to a nursing home. They were able to apply for the higher nursing home rate without involving a social worker.

These payments ceased to be available for new applicants on 1 April 1993. People who were receiving them before this date had their payments preserved. This meant that they could not be reduced or discontinued. They are usually increased slightly every April.

Changing times

On 1 April 1993 the Community Care Act was brought into force and everything changed. The local authorities started to 'purchase' residential and nursing home care. Every home was invited to submit a tender for supplying care.

Contracts were drawn up between homes and the local authority at fixed prices agreed by the home and the authority. Each fixed price became known as a contracted fee.

Receiving the old DSS payments

There are still some people in care homes receiving the old DSS payments.

If a person is in residential care they can still be transferred to a nursing home with the approval of their care manager. However, if your relative does not have a care manager, phone your local social security or care manager's office for help and advice.

Changing to DSS nursing allowance

If your relative is receiving the old DSS residential rate you can still apply, on their behalf, to have it increased to the nursing rate, but there is a snag.

There is often a shortfall between the old DSS nursing home rates and the 'contracted price' of some nursing homes.

Social services are unable to authorise the extra amount needed to pay the higher fees. The shortfall has to be made up by the resident or their family and can amount to a weekly sum of £25.00 or more. For example:

Cost of room	£320.00 per week
Less DSS	£290.00 per week
Shortfall	£30.00 per week

Pocket money

The government stipulates that every person in residential care should have money for personal spending. Currently this is £13.35 per week and is paid with the weekly DSS allowance, making a total of £303.35.

It has been a common practice in the past for the personal allowance to be seen and used as part of the fees. Although this still happens occasionally, bear in mind that if the pocket money is used in this way your relative will still need some money for toiletries, newspapers and other items not allowed for in the fees.

Many homes have an accurate accounting system of residents' pocket money deposited with them. If cash is needed your relative only has to ask the administrator or matron and sign for the money received.

Pocket money – under the new system

Personal spending money is allowed for when the financial assessment is made by the care manager.

Looking at insurance

Find out whether or not your relative's personal items are fully covered by the home's insurance.

Consider taking out additional insurance to cover valuables as most homes do not take on the responsibility for loss, theft or damage to residents' personal belongings.

CHECKLIST

- Have you compared fees with other homes?
- Have you budgeted for 'extras'?
- Is your relative getting the maximum help they are allowed?

CASE STUDIES

Peter's financial assessment

Mavis and Julia met the care manager at the hospital and were shown into a small office. Peter was brought in from the ward. Due to his mental state he was unable to contribute to the meeting.

The two sisters were aware of his financial affairs and were able to give the following information:

Weekly income:	£ p	
Retirement pension	64.48	
Occupational pension	10.22	
	74.70	
Bank balance	£1,500.00	
Other assets	his house (owned outright)	
Weekly cost of home	310.00	

Peter will get maximum income support to pay for his fees less his income of £74.70, but he will be allowed to keep pocket money, which is £13.35 a week. Therefore each week he will be allowed:

Income support	310.00	
Less: weekly income	74.70	
Add back: pocket money	13.35	
	61.35	61.35
The amount he receives will be:		£248.65

This will be made up of a contribution from the residential fund and the balance from the local authority.

When Peter starts to receive income support on a long term basis, a 'legal charge' will be placed on his property.

Mavis and Julia will need to sell Peter's cottage to:

1. reimburse the local authority for the income support Peter has received
2. pay Peter's nursing home fees.

Peter will not be eligible for further income support until his funds drop to £16,000.

Alan and Peggy discuss finances

Alan and Peggy discussed how they would manage if Peggy were to receive residential nursing care. Peggy wouldn't need agency nurses, so the money they saved could be put toward the cost of her care.

Their situation was as follows:

- Alan earns approximately £2,500 per month gross.
- Peggy's Disability Living Allowance would stop if she received income support.
- The couple have no savings.
- The contracted price of the chosen home is £320.00 per week, plus:

hairdressing	£5.50
newspapers	£3.35
toilet articles	£1.50

Alan thought he would be expected to contribute towards Peggy's fees. Extras would be paid for out of Peggy's personal spending money. Alan would continue to look after all their financial affairs.

The next day Alan asked Peggy's care manager to call and discuss whether Peggy would be eligible for any income support.

Connie's treasure

Audrey had always known that her aunt was reasonably affluent but was surprised to find out just how many assets she had.

Connie had always kept her account at the local bank. Money had been transferred to Spain as she needed it. Fifty years ago she had been left a large sum of money which she had not touched. It had gained compound interest and she was now a wealthy lady. Her income was as follows:

income on capital	£10,000 per annum
rent from leased property	£5,200 per annum
other assets – property in Spain.	

Audrey realised that Connie would not be eligible for income support. The bank would continue to administer the account but Audrey would be given power of attorney.

Fred and Annie talk to their care manager

Annie asked Elizabeth to be present at the interview. She felt it would give them moral support.

Annie told them that they rented their three bedroom house. Their mentally sub-normal son lived with them.

The care manager felt that their son, Kevin, had become too much for Annie. Annie argued that Kevin should be at home unless he was happier at the Sunshine Home. After assuring them that Kevin was very happy the care manager promised to take them to see him.

Weekly income:	retirement pension	£90.50
	private pension	£50.25
		£140.75

In addition to this they have various allowances for caring for their son. Their care manager told them that all allowances for Kevin would cease when he no longer lived at home.

The home that they have chosen is contracted with the local authority to supply nursing care at £310.00 per person sharing a room. They will be allowed £13.35 (approximately) each for pocket money.

Weekly nursing home fees @ £310.00	£620.00
Less weekly income	£140.75
	£479.25
Add back pocket money @ £13.35 each	£ 26.70
Residential allowance and income support	£505.95

As Fred is very frail now and Annie can't cope with money matters their solicitor has been appointed to look after their affairs.

DISCUSSION POINTS

- Is your relative capable of looking after their own financial affairs?
- Should a representative be appointed and if so, who?
- Should anyone apply for power of attorney?
- How much personal spending money will your relative need each week?
- Who will buy toiletries etc? How will they be paid for?
- Who will be responsible for monitoring your relative's progress?
- Will insurance be necessary to cover personal belongings?

6
Arranging Admission

VISITING BY MATRON

Generally speaking, when you and your relative have chosen the most appropriate home the matron will visit your relative to:

- introduce herself
- discover what your relative feels they need
- make her own assessment of their needs.

Occasionally, matron will decide that the home you have chosen is unsuitable and will refer you back to the care manager.

Reasons for not accepting a resident

1. Wrong category of home. Maybe they need a home that cares for elderly mentally ill persons, commonly known as EMI homes.
2. The home may not be registered, or have the right equipment for certain patients – for example, young disabled people.
3. The prospective resident may be disruptive, have behavioural problems or be excessively aggressive.

RESERVING A ROOM

Once the matron has agreed to admit your relative you will be asked for a deposit to reserve the room. This is usually non-returnable. You may be asked for:

- one month's fees
- one week's fee
- £100.00 or less.

The deposit amount is governed by the wishes of the proprietor, the management company or the accountants. Residents on income support are not always asked for a deposit. Make sure this sum will be deducted from the first invoice (see Chapter 5: Making a deposit).

Arranging date and time of admission

When a resident is to be admitted from hospital the admission date and time are usually arranged between the ward, care manager (if appropriate) and the home. It will largely depend on when transport is available, whether all the paperwork is completed and the most convenient time for the home to accept them. If you have a preference ask the ward sister if this can be taken into consideration.

Receiving the contract

Either before or soon after admission your relative should be sent, or given, a contract stating terms, conditions and fees at the time of admission. It's usually a long and sometimes complicated document but read it through carefully, making sure that you understand it (see Chapter 8).

PREPARING THE ROOM

What you can expect the staff to do

The room should have been thoroughly cleaned and look inviting. The bed will have been made up with an appropriate mattress and clean bed linen. An artificial flower arrangement may have been put in the room.

The staff should check that the call bell is working and that a full complement of furniture is in the room including a commode if needed. If the room is *en suite* your relative should be encouraged to use their own facilities if at all possible.

Most homes provide towels and face cloths and these should already be on the towel rail. A jug of fresh water and a glass will probably be within easy reach.

But the room still remains impersonal!

Making the room more homely

This depends on:

- the mental and physical state of your relative
- what they are allowed to have and what relatives are allowed to do

- whether they would like to take in some of their own furniture
- their tastes and preferences.

Some homes have the rooms decorated to the new resident's choice of colour before admission. Many homes have a colour scheme for a particular area of the home. For example, blue for one floor, peach for another and magnolia for the ground floor.

Taking personal possessions

Generally speaking residents will be allowed to take the following items provided they are in good condition and free from woodworm:

- their favourite chair, provided it meets fire regulation standards
- small items of furniture
- television
- music centre, tapes/records
- books
- hobbies and craft materials
- clock
- pictures

Note: All electrical items brought into the home will be subject to an annual safety check by the home's own electrical contractor.

Pets

- Budgies and fish tanks may be allowed, but the family will be held responsible for their cleanliness and feeding.
- Dogs/cats may be welcome to visit but probably not allowed to stay.
- Pet tarantulas, snakes and rodents would not be welcome.
- Make sure you check with matron beforehand.

Items not usually allowed

- Because of fire regulations residents may not be able to take their own linen, curtains or items of a flammable nature.
- Rugs and mats may cause frail people to fall and are therefore discouraged.
- Furniture that is dilapidated, dangerous or unsuitable.

Installing a phone

Most homes have a pay phone, which may be sufficient for your relative's needs. However, you should consider the following questions:

- Is there a mobile pay phone that can be brought to their room?
- Will it matter to them if the phone is fixed in a public place?
- Are they likely to make or receive many phone calls?
- Do they need a phone in their room?

Some homes have a phone system that allows for calls to be made from a resident's room. They are, of course, automatically charged to the resident's account.

Once it has been decided to install a phone discuss with matron what is required. This is important as there are various systems that can be used in nursing homes.

It is more than likely that you will be told to contact British Telecom to arrange for a line to be connected to the room. Your relative may choose to buy or rent the most suitable phone for their needs. They, or their attorney, would be responsible for the installation charge and subsequent telephone account.

Choosing the phone

When choosing an appropriate phone, bear the following points in mind:

- Many elderly people suffer from failing sight, so look at phones with large push buttons and figures.
- Some cannot remember phone numbers easily: you may need to look at one with a memory.
- Others have a hearing problem and may need help from special amplifiers. BT or the nearest 'Hi' Centre will be able to help.
- A few residents like to take the phone wherever they go: a cordless phone might be the answer.

Due to new technology it is impossible to keep up to date with all the new equipment on the market. Visit the phone shops and see for yourself what is the best phone for them.

Keeping the handyman busy

The handyman is responsible for maintenance and any odd jobs that residents may need to have done. He is the only authorised person covered by insurance to do this work. Therefore he is the only person allowed to do general maintenance work and DIY jobs in the home.

Matron will ensure that he will put up pictures and shelves and carry out any repairs that may be required. Discuss any needs with the matron or nurse in charge.

Other things you can do

Everything is ready for your relative's admission. They are expected at 2 pm. Only the final touches are left to be done:

- set out their things on the dressing table
- bring in and arrange a few fresh flowers
- write out a 'Good luck in your new home' card and leave it for them
- leave a bottle of their favourite squash with the jug of water
- put a few pieces of fruit in a basket
- anything else that will help them to settle in
- best of all, be there yourself, if possible, when they arrive.

MOVING YOUR RELATIVE

Hospital transport can be arranged for dependent patients transferring from the ward to a local home. This is particularly useful if they are wheelchair or bed-bound. However, depending on the health of your relative, you may be asked, or you may prefer, to take them to the home yourself.

If you are contemplating transporting your relative yourself, consider:

- Your car insurance – will it cover you to do this?
- Is your car suitable for your relative's needs?
- Can you manage to care for them on the journey?
- Could someone else come with you in case of difficulty?
- Could you take them by taxi if hospital transport is unavailable? (Private ambulance services are available but may be costly.)

CHECKLIST

- Have you asked matron to have pictures/shelves put up?

- Is your relative's clothing adequate and suitable for the season?
- Have you marked all their clothing and personal items?
- Have you made a 'property list' of the items they are taking?
- Have you insured their personal effects?
- Have you taken photos of valuable items for insurance purposes?
- Have you been able to mark your relative's name on their dentures and spectacles?

CASE STUDIES

A new home for Peter

Mavis and Julia liked the Ashcroft nursing home and felt that their father would be happy living there. Matron had visited Peter and had agreed to admit him to the home.

Peter's care manager had been informed of the choice of home. It took several days to complete the financial and needs assessment. Eventually all the paperwork was complete. The hospital arranged transport to take Peter to the home in two days' time.

Mavis tried to interest her father in the move but he remained apathetic and uninterested. The two sisters took a few framed photographs from his house to be hung on his wall.

They knew he was fond of flowers and took in a fresh flower arrangement to greet him.

Peggy wants to stay at the Brambles Nursing Home

Peggy was already staying at the Brambles on a temporary basis. She had settled in well and wanted to stay there. Four of the other residents were in their early 50s and suffering from MS. Peggy seemed to be in a more advanced stage than the others, but she had made friends with them

The home seemed to have plenty of staff and modern equipment, which Peggy appreciated.

The day that Peggy was admitted she had been pleasantly surprised. Some of the other residents were having a sing-song in the lounge and everybody seemed to be enjoying themselves. She had not expected that.

Although she was well looked after she still didn't feel as though the Brambles was her home.

Peggy's care manager visited her to tell her that she could stay permanently, if she wanted to. The paperwork had been completed and authorisation for her to stay had arrived from the local authority.

Peggy decided she would like to stay at the Brambles indefinitely. Later that evening she asked Alan to make arrangements with matron to bring in her bed and other things that she wanted.

Connie might go to Cloisters

Connie did like Cloisters. She loved the room and the garden. She imagined how the room would look when she had installed the furniture she had brought. Matron gave her a conducted tour and agreed to admit her as soon as she was fit enough to leave hospital.

She was impatient with Audrey for asking all 'those stupid questions' as she put it. Audrey made arrangements for her aunt to be admitted on a trial basis. If she was happy she could stay permanently.

As Connie was staying on a temporary basis matron asked for the fee to be paid in advance. Connie agreed and paid by cheque.

Arranging Annie and Fred's move

Annie was now well enough to leave hospital. The ward staff thought it would be better for her to move into the Devonshire Complex a few days before Fred. She could then rest after being transferred without worrying about Fred's needs. Everybody knew that she would find it difficult to allow the nurses to do the things for Fred that she had always done.

Elizabeth discussed transport arrangements with the ward sister, who said she would contact the home and the care manager. She would then arrange hospital transport to take Annie to the Devonshire Complex in two days' time. The ward sister also agreed to liaise with her colleague on Fred's ward so that he would arrive two days after Annie.

The following day Elizabeth took a few pictures and photographs, a large print Bible and a radio to put in Annie and Fred's new room. She saw the matron and told her that Annie and Fred liked a daily paper and that Annie had been a regular reader of a popular weekly magazine. Matron said she would ask the newsagent to add these to his delivery list starting on the following day ready for Annie when she arrived.

On the way home Elizabeth bought some flowers to make an arrangement to take in to welcome Annie. She decided not to give Annie a 'New Home' card in case it upset her as she was hoping to go home after a month's stay.

DISCUSSION POINTS

1. Should your relative take valuable items with them?

2. Is it necessary to take out insurance for any valuables?

3. Who will prepare the room and be there when your relative arrives?

4. Who will arrange transport to the home?

5. Will the new resident need a phone?

7
Deciding What to Take

MAKING DIFFICULT DECISIONS

Deciding what they should take into the nursing home is probably one of the most difficult decisions your relative will ever have to make.

It's always sad to dispose of knick-knacks that have been around for years, especially when they hold fond memories. Encourage them to decide what is essential, what they want to keep and what they can do without.

LISTING PERSONAL DETAILS

Perhaps the first item on the agenda should be to make a list of all their personal details. This will be invaluable on the day of admission.

Soon after your relative's arrival a nurse will come round to ask them or you for the following information. Most people find it difficult to remember where Mum was born or what her maiden name was, so it is easier for you if you have all the information written down in readiness.

Information you may be asked for

- your relative's full name and maiden name, if applicable
- date of birth and place of birth if known
- name, address and phone numbers of next of kin
- names and phone numbers of other contacts
- your relative's medical history and current state of health
- name, address and phone number of their doctor
- how they like to be addressed
- details of special diet, for instance in relation to diabetes
- their food likes, dislikes and allergies

- details of cuts, bruises or sores
- their religion and whether they practise their faith
- whether they smoke and if so how many and when
- whether they have alcoholic drinks and if so when

The nurse will ask for any medicines they are taking and for a letter from your doctor or hospital if you were given one.

Disposal arrangements

Some matrons ask questions regarding funeral arrangements which are noted for use when your relative passes away. You may find this strange. However, the following information is essential if death occurs unexpectedly:

- Have your relative's organs been donated for medical science?
- Who is to be contacted regarding the donation?
- Are any special arrangements required by their religion?
- What are your relative's wishes regarding burial or cremation?
- Who is the chosen funeral director? (It is helpful to know if it will be a prearranged funeral – for example, Chosen Heritage or similar. Information leaflets regarding prearranged funerals can be obtained from the Post Office or Age Concern).

This personal information is needed so that their wishes can be carried out if, for any reason, you are unavailable when the inevitable happens.

Walking aids and wheelchairs

If your relative has been supplied with a zimmer frame or similar walking aid by the hospital's physiotherapy department, it may have to be returned when they are admitted to a nursing home. Sometimes the home is unable to supply a replacement, in which case you may be able to borrow one from your local branch of the Red Cross Society. Alternatively it may be better to buy one.

Wheelchairs provided by the social services remain with the person for as long as they are needed. If they have been supplied with an electric wheelchair ensure that there is enough space for them to use it. Return it to social services if it is no longer required. They will collect it, free of charge, at your request.

CHOOSING SUITABLE CLOTHING

The amount your relative can take will be governed by the amount of wardrobe and drawer space they are allocated. Most rooms have either a single wardrobe and a chest of drawers or dressing table or a combination wardrobe. The latter is more compact but has less space.

Type of clothing to take

This will depend on:

- the season
- activities (outdoor)
- your relative's comfort
- their ability to cope with normal clothing when dressing. Arthritic people find it painful to squeeze into conventional clothing.

When buying new clothing consider:

- Is it washable or dry clean only?
- Can it be washed in a washing machine?
- Can it be tumble dried?
- Is it colour fast?
- Will it shrink with washing?
- Is thermal underwear really necessary? It does not always wash well in commercial machines.

Hand wash and dry clean only

These items sometimes get mixed up with machine washable laundry and are ruined. You may be asked to care for these garments yourself. If the home undertakes to send them for dry cleaning the cost will almost certainly be passed on to your relative.

Making the selection

It's difficult to know how much or what kind of clothing another person needs. Touching their skin might give you an indication whether they are too cold or too hot, but you can't actually experience it.

Look at their current clothing: it will provide the best indication of your relative's needs and the style they like to wear.

Sometimes clothing is old and beyond repair, in which case try to replace it with equivalent garments, providing they were suitable in the first place. Remember that, although they may have been adequate when your relative bought them, the same type may not be suitable for them now.

Pure woollen clothing, particularly underwear, can cause allergic reactions and irritation in some people.

Figure 11 is a basic list that you may like to customise to suit your relative's needs.

MARKING PERSONAL POSSESSIONS

Mark personal property (see Figure 12) and all personal clothing to prevent loss when being laundered. Most methods of marking have disadvantages:

- marking pen: tends to fade and needs renewing frequently
- Indian ink: remains stable but is difficult to use
- woven name tapes: stitching needs to be checked often
- printed name tapes: tends to fade with frequent washing
- glued-on tapes: glue does not always withstand frequent washing, needs to be checked often
- iron-on tapes: sometimes come off after two or three washes.

Cigarettes and alcohol

Matron may ask for these items to be marked and left in the office to be given out as required. This is because some residents are not well enough to take control of them and need help when smoking or drinking.

- Due to fire risk smoking is usually confined to special areas within the home.

Reading, hobbies, jigsaw puzzles and crafts

Your relative will be encouraged to take some of their books and any hobbies that they enjoy:

- Personalised labels are useful for books.
- Hobbies can be kept in marked containers.
- Jigsaw puzzles can be kept in their boxes secured with elastic bands.

Lady		Gentleman	
Basic underwear and nightwear			
Vests	4	Vests	4
Knickers	6 pairs	Underpants	6 pairs
Tights/stockings	6 pairs	Socks	6 pairs
Bras (if worn)	3		
Suspender belts	3		
Corsets (if worn)	3		
Slips/half slips	4		
Nightdress/pyjamas	4	Pyjamas	4 pairs
Bed jackets	2		
Dressing gowns	1-2	Dressing gowns	1-2
Slippers/shoes	1-2 pairs	Slippers/shoes	1-2 pairs
Bed socks (if worn)	2 pairs	Bed socks	2 pairs
Basic top clothing			
Dresses	3	Trousers	4 pairs
Skirts/trousers	2-3	Shirts	6
Blouses/T-shirts	2-3	Tie	1
Cardigans/jumpers	3	Sweaters	2
Leisure suits if preferred		Leisure suits if preferred	
For outside activities if applicable			
Coat or jacket	1	Coat or jacket	1
Hat and scarf	1	Hat and scarf	1
Gloves	1 pair	Gloves	1 pair
Outdoor shoes	1 pair	Outdoor shoes	1 pair

Each person is an individual and has their own needs. These lists should be adjusted to suit your relative's requirements.

Fig. 11. List of basic clothing needs.

False limbs	Can be named with a marking or paint pen.
False eyes	Do not usually go astray.
Dentures	These can't be satisfactorily marked by the general public. Take them to your dental surgeon who can arrange for this to be done by a dental technician. This will incur a charge.
Hearing aids	There are various types of these with differing amounts of space in which to mark them. You may be able to write initials on the appliance with a paint pen.
Spectacles	Seek the optician's advice or try small self-adhesive labels.
Walking aids (zimmer frame, tripod *etc*)	Tie-on labels can be used but tend to disappear. Self-adhesive labels or paint pen is more permanent.
Wooden stick	Paint pen or a personalised decorative walking stick badge.
Wheelchairs	Paint pen. Check frequently.

Most other items – for instance, televisions, 'helping hands' or radios – can be marked with paint/marking pen or self-adhesive labels.

Fig. 12. Ways of marking personal property.

You may like to buy your relative a folding tray for jigsaw puzzles or a book stand for holding heavier books.

Buying bathroom toiletries

Favourite toiletries help to boost your relative's morale, sustain self esteem and maintain individuality.

The list in Figure 13, which is not exhaustive, offers suggestions for items which you feel are appropriate for your relative to take.

Lady	Gentleman
2 face flannels	2 face flannels
2 body flannels	2 body flannels
Bubble bath	Bubble bath
Soap	Soap
Talcum powder	Talcum powder
Lady shave	Razor
Nail varnish and remover	Shaving soap/cream
Antiperspirant/deodorant	Antiperspirant/deodrant
Body spray/perfume	After shave
Shampoo, conditioner, setting aids	Shaving brush
Cosmetics/beauty treatments	Shampoo
Brush and comb	Brush and comb
Toothbrush and toothpaste	Toothbrush and toothpaste
Denture cleaner	Denture cleaner

Fig. 13. List of toiletries.

Pets

If your relative is allowed to take in a budgie or other pet (see Chapter 6) they will need food and dishes, bedding if appropriate and all other equipment necessary for the wellbeing of the animal. All their pet's vaccinations should be done before being 'admitted'. It's a good idea to take details of the pet's diet, vet and the date when vaccinations are due.

If their pet has to be left behind your relative may worry about the animal's welfare. A photograph from the new owner and a short note about the health and happiness of the animal will put their mind at rest. A visit from their pet, with matron's permission, is even better.

Choosing furniture and pictures

Personal items will stamp your relative's room with their own individuality. Encourage them to choose some of their favourite pictures, photographs, and furniture to take. Let them take time to ponder on the merits and sentimental value of each item.

- Remember they will only have one room.
- Leave enough space for staff to attend to their needs.

Spending money

Unless there is a 'trolley shop' or willing staff to do shopping there will be little to spend their money on. Daily papers and hairdressing is generally added to the account. However, they might prefer to pay the hairdresser themselves. Think about this when deciding how much spending money they will need each week.

Keeping important items

Residents should not take items such as cheque books, building society pass books or credit/bank cards in case they get lost or stolen. If your relative insists on taking them try to persuade them to give them to the matron for safe keeping. Make a note of card and cheque book details in case of loss.

Wills, house deeds and other important documents can be lodged at the bank or with their solicitor.

CHECKLIST

- Has your relative decided what to take with them?
- Are all the relevant possessions marked?
- Does your relative understand the house rules about drinking alcohol and smoking?

CASE STUDIES

Peter likes a smoke and a drink

Although Peter had become apathetic and didn't really know his daughters, they noticed that he still smoked occasionally. One evening while he was still in hospital Mavis asked the ward sister if she could bring him in a tot of brandy. She remembered he always used to have an evening drink of warm milk laced with brandy.

Sister agreed and from then on Mavis took her father a small drink each evening which he seemed to enjoy.

When arranging his admission to the Ashcroft nursing home Mavis mentioned this to matron. She suggested that Mavis left a half bottle, with his name and solely for his enjoyment.

Peggy has a special wheelchair and bed

Peggy was worried. She needed her Mediscus bed to prevent her getting pressure sores but it was very large. Would she be able to have it brought in, she wondered. And what about her wheelchair? That was big too.

Alan said he would ask matron. He made a special journey to see her. He was reassured when he was shown the double doors that opened into Peggy's new abode. He went back to Peggy and set her mind at rest.

Connie wants everything and goes shopping

Connie had brought very little back to England with her. It had been left for Audrey to go and sort out later. Connie saw it as an opportunity to buy new clothing and furniture.

After much persuasion Connie bought just a small antique escritoire and bookcase. Her clothes were hardly suitable for the English climate so Audrey and her aunt went into Marks & Spencer to buy essential underwear, nightwear and day clothes.

Connie could expand her wardrobe later, Audrey informed her. Matron was advised that the furniture would be arriving the following day. She told Audrey to take out sufficient insurance cover in case of theft or damage.

Annie loves her pets

Elizabeth couldn't help but notice that Annie wasn't as happy as usual. She tried to find out why but Annie would say nothing. After spending an hour in her company Elizabeth went to talk to Fred.

She asked him if he knew what had upset his wife. After some thought he said that he thought it was probably because she would miss Tessa, their budgie, and Sooty the cat.

Before saying anything to either of them about the problem Elizabeth went to see matron. She agreed that the budgie could stay in the home but as there was already a resident cat Sooty would not be welcome.

Thinking about the problem, Elizabeth suddenly remembered Mrs Matthew, one of the church members. She loved cats, always had a houseful of them, and, on hearing about Sooty, she was only too pleased to help out.

Before going to see Annie the next day Elizabeth collected Sooty from the cattery and took him to Mrs Matthew's house.

Annie brightened up considerably when her friend told her what she had done. Elizabeth felt pleased the problem had been sorted.

DISCUSSION POINTS

1. Is the room large enough for all your relative wants to take?

2. How will the furniture be transported?

3. What will happen to any pets?

4. Where will important documents (house deeds, will *etc*) be lodged?

5. Pocket money: how much will your relative need? How will it get topped up?

8
Signing a Contract

UNDERSTANDING THE CONTRACT

A contract is a binding formal agreement between two or more parties. The word 'contract' is often used to refer to a document which sets out the terms of such an agreement.

The home gives a copy of the contract to new residents so that they know the basic terms under which they are admitted. If the terms of the contract are not adhered to by the home you can make a complaint on behalf of your relative. Similarly if the terms are not met by your relative they will be asked to comply with what they have agreed. If this is impossible for them and there is no alternative, you could be asked to find them other accommodation.

Figure 14 shows some items that could be covered in a contract.

Before April 1993

If your relative had needed nursing home care before April 1993 they would have chosen a nursing home, applied to the DHSS, filled in the appropriate forms and returned them. It was almost certain that funding would then be given. Once admitted your relative would have received the same residents' contract as everybody else.

Since April 1993

Before the new laws governing funding came into force all nursing homes were invited to state what care they could offer and to submit a tender to their local authority for providing it. Tenders were based on cost of food, lighting and heating, staff salaries, cleaning and laundry, utilities, and all the other expenses involved in running a nursing home. Some managements elected to run private establishments and did not either submit a tender or enter into a contract with the local authority.

When all tenders had been received, contracts were offered to homes providing good care at acceptable fees.

If there is a contract between the local authority and your relative's preferred home then a contract may not be offered to residents on

Fees	Amount, when payable, how to pay
House rules	What residents can and can't do
Absences	Holding residents' rooms
Discharge	Notice of leaving
Death of a resident	When the room has to be cleared by
Notice	Notice from the home terminating the contract Notice from a resident terminating the contract
Nuisances	Noise
Complaints	How to make a complaint
Gratuities	To staff
Extra payments	Hairdressing, chiropody
Insurance	The home's insurance, personal insurance
Disclaimer	Denial of responsibility for personal belongings

Fig. 14. What might be in a contract.

income support. Because everything is covered in the home's contract with the local authority most proprietors/managers feel that a contract between themselves and residents is unnecessary. If a contract is offered it will differ slightly from the one given to self-funding residents. Nursing home inspectors would like all residents to have a contract between themselves and the home of their choice, whether they are self-funding or receiving income support.

AGREEING CONTRACTED FEES

The fees that your relative has agreed to pay will be known as their contracted fee. If they are self-funding there will be no complications, but if their fees are to be paid by the local authority the proprietor or manager may ask for a 'top up' (extra money):

- if your relative wants a superior room to one offered at the contracted price
- to bring fees of residents receiving income support into line with self-funding residents.

Contracted fees were introduced by local authorities to prevent homes asking for 'top ups' to raise fees. If your relative is asked for a 'top up', for any reason, discuss it with their care manager before agreeing to pay it.

Any 'top ups' that are agreed must be written into the contract.

Missing or damaged belongings

Almost all contracts will have a clause releasing the home from any responsibility for residents' property that is lost, stolen or damaged within the home – for example, lost jewellery, valuables and money or clothing damaged by washing.

The contract will explain about the home's insurance which is often very little or non-existent for residents' personal effects.

Damaging the property

Some proprietors insert a clause into the contract that gives them the right to claim for any damage caused by the resident or their family. If this is signed by your relative a claim can be made from their estate.

You may be asked to sign on your relative's behalf if they are incapable of doing so themselves. Be careful. If there is no estate and you have agreed to this clause by signing the contract, you may become liable for any damage caused by your relative or their visitors.

The inspector of nursing homes

The contract should also give the name and address and phone number of the inspector of nursing homes for the area or at least tell you how to contact him or her.

BEFORE SIGNING

- Make sure you, or your relative, reads and understands the contract.
- If a clause causes you concern ask if it can be taken out.
- Ask matron to clarify ambiguous clauses.
- If in doubt, take the contract to a solicitor.
- Remember the signed contract is a legal and binding document.
- Don't let anybody sign the contract unless everyone concerned is satisfied with the terms and conditions stated.

Witnessing the signature

Most contracts ask for an independent witness to be present when the contract is signed. He/she will then sign to say they saw the resident, or the representative, sign the contract. It does not make them liable in any way.

CHECKLIST

- Have you asked the matron to clarify ambiguous clauses in the contract?
- Do you and your relative fully understand the contract?
- Do you know how to contact the local health authority inspector of nursing homes?

CASE STUDIES

Mavis gets a clause removed

Mavis and Julia discussed their father's contract which they had just received. There was only one clause that bothered them. It stated that if they signed the document they could become liable for any damage caused by their father. It wouldn't cause a problem until all his money had gone and even then it would be unlikely that he would do that much damage. Despite this they thought they would feel happier if it was removed from the contract. Mavis spoke to the matron about it and she agreed to delete the clause.

Peggy gets a contract

Just before Peggy was due to be admitted to the Brambles Nursing Home she received a contract ready for her signature.

Alan looked at it carefully. The fees were much higher than they had been told they would be. He phoned the matron, who said she would look into the matter.

Later that day matron phoned to tell him there had been an error and a new contract would be sent to him. Alan thanked her and was relieved that he had read the contract before it was signed.

Connie signs her contract

Audrey read her aunt's contract and although she didn't have any queries she decided to send it to Connie's solicitor to check.

When the solicitor returned the document he gave permission for it to be signed. Audrey explained the contents of the contract to her aunt. She then asked a friend to witness her aunt sign the document. Her friend then added her own signature and address.

Annie is surprised

Annie was given her contract soon after she and Fred were admitted.

'But we're only here for a month,' she exclaimed.

'You still need to have a contract,' the matron told her. She went on to explain that the contract confirmed the basic cost of the room she shared with Fred, details of extras and what was and what was not allowed within the home.

Annie agreed to read it and show it to Elizabeth. She and Fred would sign if they found the contract to be satisfactory.

DISCUSSION POINTS

1. Does everybody concerned understand the contract?

2. Are there any clauses in the contract that worry you?

3. Should you use a solicitor to check your relative's contract?

4. Has your relative been asked for a 'top up?'

5. If the answer is yes, what are you going to do about it?

CLOISTERS NURSING HOME

Conditions of Admission and Terms of Business

Name of Resident:

Date of birth:

Date of admittance:

****

1. A letter from a General Practitioner or Hospital Consultant might be required to accompany the resident on admission.

2. All drugs, medications, ointments/creams and inhalations must be handed in to the senior nurse on admission. Relatives and visitors are asked not to bring in any medications or food without consulting the Matron.

3. Residents are asked to discuss smoking arrangements and alcoholic drink requirements prior to admission.

4. The weekly fees are currently £.......... per person and are due for payment at the date of invoice. We reserve the right to charge interest at the rate of interest of 2% above the minimum lending rate of the National Westminster Bank PLC for the time being in force on any sums still outstanding 30 days after the date of invoicing. Fees are subject to review from time to time.

5. Fees, unless otherwise stated, include accommodation, full board and laundering of personal items. Registration with doctors can be private, in which case the supply of drugs/medications will also be private and the appropriate charges will be made. Residents treated under the NHS will receive medical attention, drugs/medications as available under the NHS. Other services and personal requirements can be arranged on request and will be charged to the resident's account.

6. Visiting times are kept as flexible as possible. The most convenient times are 11 am to 7 pm each day. If you wish to visit at other times, please contact the Matron. Whilst visiting, if you wish to talk privately, the Matron will be happy to make any necessary arrangements.

Fig. 15. Sample nursing home contract.

7. Our existing insurance policy covers effects up to a maximum of £500.00 per resident. If property of greater value is retained and, in particular furs, jewellery *etc* they must be covered by the resident's own insurance. Every care is taken but residents are asked not to keep excessive sums of cash or valuable items in their rooms. A detailed list of such items must be handed in on admission and updated as appropriate thereafter. Valuables can be locked away for safe-keeping when not in use on request to the Matron. No responsibility can be taken for personal possessions not clearly and permanently named. For clothing items this must be woven name tape, stitched on securely.

8. Residence in our Nursing Home does not constitute a tenancy within the meanings of the Rent Act. We therefore reserve the right to terminate the licence to occupy a bed or room in the Home on formal written notice of four weeks. On the resident's side termination of occupation must be given by the same length of notice in writing, unless the resident's stay is for a predetermined period.

9. Queries and complaints, if any, should be addressed to the Matron. If further queries or complaints arise these should be referred to:- The Health Authority Inspector of Nursing Homes (address available on request).

10. In the event that a resident vacates the room permanently for whatever reason, we reserve the right to make a vacant room charge not exceeding one month's fee, where notice has not or cannot be given, unless the room is otherwise occupied.

In the case of temporary absence of one week the fees will be payable for the retention of the room. If the absence is longer than one week the fee will be subject to a reduction of £10.00 per week for the period of the absence.

11. Management cannot accept responsibility for residents' personal finances, but we are always willing to discuss and advise when requested. (Information regarding financial assistance with fees is also available if required.)

Continued

RESIDENT'S NAME: ____________________ Date of Birth: __________

RELIGION ____

NEXT OF KIN ____

RELATIONSHIP TO RESIDENT ______________________________

FULL NAME ____

ADDRESS ____

____

______________________________ POST CODE: __________

TELEPHONE NUMBERS: HOME __________ WORK __________

OTHER CONTACTS:

______________________________ TELEPHONE __________

______________________________ TELEPHONE __________

______________________________ TELEPHONE __________

==

PLEASE READ THE CONDITIONS ABOVE BEFORE SIGNING THE FORM. FAILURE TO DO SO DOES NOT EXCUSE YOU FROM COMPLIANCE WITH THEM.

==

I/We* have read the conditions of admission and will ensure that the above named resident complies with them and will indemnify the Home against any breach thereof.

RESIDENT'S/REPRESENTATIVE'S SIGNATURE: __________

WITNESSED BY: ______________ SIGNATURE ______________

ADDRESS ____

______________________________ DATE __________________

NAME AND ADDRESS OF:
SOLICITOR/POWER OF ATTORNEY______________________

____

______________________________ POST CODE: __________

TELEPHONE NUMBER: ____________________________________

FAMILY UNDERTAKER: __________ TELEPHONE __________

BURIAL/CREMATION/OTHER ______________________________

*please delete as appropriate.

9
Applying for a Grant

FULFILLING THE CONDITIONS

It may have been suggested that your relative should apply for a grant from a charitable organisation. Whether they are likely to qualify depends on:

1. Your relative's financial status.
2. Whether they are claiming income support.
3. Their needs.

If your relative is claiming income support to assist with nursing home fees you must tell their care manager if they get any extra income. Grants resulting from applications to charities are counted as extra income and may reduce the amount of income support your relative is eligible for.

Being self financed

While your relative is paying their own fees, a one-off or recurrent grant (weekly or monthly sums) will not cause a problem. However, should your relative ever need to apply for income support, grants from charities will be taken into consideration. You may find that the amount of income support they can claim is reduced by the sum of money they receive from the charity.

Paying for a better room

Your relative may be tempted to go for a room that is better than one offered at the contracted price of the local authority. You can apply, on your relative's behalf, to a charitable organisation for a grant to help pay the extra cost. It might be possible to use a grant for this purpose without losing part of their income support. However, you should discuss this with their care manager before applying.

APPROACHING A CHARITABLE ORGANISATION

If you approach a charitable organisation on behalf of your relative they will do their best to help out. They will, of course, only be able to help applicants that are eligible. For example, if the charity stipulates 'poor and elderly people who live in Scotland', it's no good applying for somebody poor and elderly who lives in England.

When you apply for a grant make sure that it is to an appropriate charity – for example, if your relative was a teacher apply to a charity that caters for teachers.

Types of grant

Your relative may be offered a one-off grant (or vouchers) for specific items, such as clothing or repairs to a piece of equipment.

Some offer a recurrent grant, which is generally a regular sum of money sent weekly or monthly for a period of time. It could be for weeks, months or even for your relative's lifetime.

Due to their commitments some charities are unable to give any financial support.

Reviewing what's on offer

- Discuss with your relative and the family what's on offer before any extra expenses are taken on.
- Ask the organisation whether the grant is a one-off sum or a recurrent payment.
- Find out how much they will award your relative each month.
- Ask how long the charity intends to give your relative support.

You will get a letter giving you full details of the support they are offering. If you have any questions telephone the charity concerned.

Getting their personal details

Before you try to obtain financial help this way you will need to know some details of your relative's and their partner's life.

Talk to them, find out about their previous occupation(s), for example, school teacher, nurse, printer *etc*; how long they worked in their trade or profession; their date and place of birth, and current financial position.

Finding organisations that might help

- Be prepared to spend an afternoon in your main library.

- Take a notebook and pen with you.
- Go to the reference section.
- Look for books giving the names of charitable organisations.
- Ask the librarian to help you find any they have.
- If the librarian does not hold such a book ask them to order one from another branch.

Reference books cannot usually be borrowed. Research will have to be carried out in the library. Some of the bigger books can be confusing and you will need time to discover how the charities are listed. One book you might ask for is *A guide to grants for individuals in need* edited by David Casson and Paul Brown, published by Director of Social Change. This book can be bought from booksellers, price approximately £15.00. You will need to place an order for it. The bookseller may be able to give you other titles to consider.

Looking for the right organisation
Once you have the book, browse through it, then look for the sections that are most likely to offer help.

Occupational charities
Look for the list of charities that cater for the occupation that your relative and or their partner did prior to their retirement: for instance, printing, nursing, physiotherapy, police force *etc.*

Service and ex-service charities
If your relative has been a member of the armed services (including national service) you should look at the section that gives details of these charities.

Geographical charities
Look at the area where your relative lives. There are many charities that cater for needy people in a given area. It may be a town, village or parish that is singled out.

These are just a few types of charities. There are thousands of others. If you need further advice regarding local charities, visit your local Citizens' Advice Bureau, who may be able to tell you what is available. They may also help you to apply either by letter or by an appropriate form.

Nursing homes owned and managed by charitable organisations

Many organisations have their own charities – for example, The Royal Masonic Benevolent Institution and the Royal British Legion. Some of them own and manage care homes but usually give preference to members or their immediate families. It doesn't mean that you're admitted free of charge but help and advice will be given where possible.

Religious denominations

Some religious denominations have their own homes, but some of them only cater for church leaders, such as vicars. Others admit church members.

There are homes that have a strong religious input and offer spiritual as well as physical healing. Residents needing long term care are not always catered for. This type of home may not be able to offer care at local authority contracted prices.

If your relative is convinced that respite care in this type of home would benefit them if they had the means, you may be able to obtain a one-off grant to help pay their fees.

APPLYING TO A CHARITY

There are six steps to making an application:

1. Phone the organisation and check the name of the person to whom you should apply.
2. Write a letter stating your relative's circumstances and needs (see Figure 16).
3. If they send you an application form, fill it in accurately and sign it.
4. Enclose any required documentation to support the application.
5. Return everything with a covering note as soon as possible.
6. Apply to several of the most likely organisations.

As your relative's needs will probably be discussed by a committee it may take a few weeks before you receive an answer.

Mr S Lynam, Director
The Hoppers Charitable Society
Bently House
Hag Lane
Caterham

6 Stripey Lane
Tunbridge Wells
Kent
Tel:
17 July 19xx

Dear Sir

I'm writing on behalf of my father, who requires assistance with nursing home fees.

His name is ....
He was born on 20 June 1908.

Upon leaving Strutts school in Dartford, he worked for 40 years in Fleet Street, firstly as a compositor and subsequently as a manager for a company specialising in newspaper advertisements.

Unfortunately, his employment was non-pensionable, and when he retired due to ill health, he received only a small union pension which ceased some time ago. He then took on a small off-licence and grocery business, which after two years proved financially unviable.

My parents bought a cottage in Devon and moved there five years prior to his retirement. During this time he worked firstly as a cellarman in a hotel in Axminster and then for small printing companies in the area. He continued to work after his retirement until ill health forced my parents to sell the cottage and move into a warden assisted elderly people's complex.

After the death of my mother my father lived on his own for a further two years before he became quite ill. He was unable to cope adequately, even with the help of the warden, home help and meals on wheels *etc*. He was admitted to hospital where he remained for a month. After making a remarkable recovery, he was transferred to a residential home for the elderly, run by the City Council.

At first all was well. Owing to the fact that my father was unable to communicate sensibly with the other residents and that my visits were infrequent due to living so far away he became depressed. He also developed other ailments resulting in a lack of activity. The consequence was a circulatory problem that affected his right foot. Last month he was admitted to the Royal Infirmary where he underwent surgery for a below-knee amputation. He is now convalescing and attending physiotherapy with a view to having an artificial limb fitted. However, either with such a prosthesis or being wheelchair-bound, he will require nursing care for the remainder of his life.

I am therefore trying to secure a place for him in a local nursing home. He has savings of £4,500 and his only income is the interest from this and his state retirement pension.

The basic fees required by the homes with vacancies range from £300-£500 per week. I am, however, still looking in an endeavour to find something less expensive. I understand that the DSS will make a contribution and my father's savings will make up the difference, but only for a short time before it runs out.

I would therefore greatly appreciate any assistance you can give.

Yours faithfully

Fig. 16. Sample letter to charities. This letter was sent out to two organisations in the early 1990s and long term financial assistance was granted. Names and addresses have been changed.

Mrs Z Lynam, Director
Appropriate Charitable Society
Bentley House
Another Street
Anytown

'Highfield'
64 Any Street
Nonsuch Town
Anywhere XY0 Z01
Telephone 0100 00000

17 October 19xx

Mrs Lynam

I am writing on behalf of my friend who needs money for new winter clothing.

Her full name is Mrs Annie Drew.

She was born in Anytown on 24 May 1925.

She left school when she was 15 years of age and worked as a children's nanny until she married at the age of 35. She has never been in pensionable employment.

Since her marriage she has cared for her son, now age 30, who has learning difficulties. A few years ago her husband lost his sight in a road accident and has since developed carcinoma of the bowel for which he has undergone surgery. He is now very frail.

Annie recently had a heart attack. She is almost ready to be discharged from hospital. Fred, her husband, was also admitted as he needs constant care. Kevin, their son, has been admitted to Sunshine House. The couple have no other relatives whatsoever.

Annie and Fred are being transferred to the nursing wing in The Devonshire Complex as soon as they are considered fit enough.

Annie has no suitable clothing to take with her. Although what she has is clean and well looked after, it's threadbare, well patched, darned and has no warmth left in it.

There has been little money coming into the home during the last few years and what there has has been spent on essentials such as food and heating. Anything left over has been spent on their son's needs.
I would be grateful if you could offer some assistance in order that Annie can have some warm clothing for the coming winter months.

Yours sincerely

Elizabeth Green

Fig. 16. Continued.

CHECKLIST

- Is it necessary to apply for a grant for your relative?
- Have you applied to suitable charitable organisations for a grant?
- Have you checked with your relative's care manager how a grant will affect your relative's income support?

CASE STUDIES

- Mavis and Julia thought that a grant was unnecessary.
- Alan and Peggy did not apply for a grant.
- Connie had more than enough money for her needs.

Elizabeth applies for a grant

Annie asked Elizabeth to pack some clothes ready to take to Cloisters.

Annie, Fred and Kevin had always dressed reasonably well, not ultra smart or fashionable, but in good serviceable clothing. Elizabeth was, therefore, quite shocked to see the state of their underwear. It was perfectly clean but old and threadbare. She thought that Annie must have spent half her life darning and repairing. Elizabeth guessed that most of their money must have been spent on buying things for Kevin.

Elizabeth decided she would apply for a grant for clothes to one of the charitable organisations. She visited the Citizens' Advice Bureau who gave her information about a local charity she could approach. The adviser helped her to compose a letter applying for a grant (see page 103) and told her they might send a form for her to complete.

In the meantime Elizabeth also planned to go to the main library to look for a book of charitable organisations that might be able to help.

DISCUSSION POINTS

1. Is it worth trying to get a grant?
2. Should the family seek financial help from a charity?
3. What kind of help: a 'one-off' grant or regular income?
4. Who will find out which charitable organisation to approach?
5. Who will apply for a grant?
6. Can your relative manage without a grant if the application is refused?

10
Overcoming Difficulties

BEATING STRESS

Experts tell us that moving home is one of the most stressful events in life. Unfortunately, moving a relative into a nursing home affects not only them but also you and the rest of the family as well.

Relieving your own stress

If you are the person who has made the arrangements you will worry that something or everything will go wrong, that your relative will not like the home or the staff will not like them. All the things that could go wrong churn around in your mind chasing positive thoughts away. This is worse if your relative grumbles about it and blames you for 'making' them move into a nursing home.

Take time off to:

- relax
- join in yoga class or keep fit regime
- walk: take the dog with you, if you have one
- read, 'cat nap' or whatever you feel like doing for an hour
- some people can find succour through prayer
- a chat to a minister of religion can often put things into perspective
- talk about any problems to somebody else; maybe they have gone through this experience themselves and can offer helpful advice
- discuss everything with other family members – let them shoulder some of the responsibility.

Understanding your relative's stress

Try to remember that their stress may cause fluctuating mood changes. It can be part of grieving for the loss of physical ability, their home and independence.

Grieving can make them:

- depressed
- angry
- frustrated because nobody will believe they can manage at home
- feel that they are 'being put away'
- feel worthless and isolated
- fearful of the pending loss of freedom and independence
- suicidal.

This can lead to:

- loss of appetite
- weight loss
- tearfulness
- loss of interest
- aggression
- discontentment.

Taking a positive view

On the other hand, if they take a positive view they will become more contented, helpful and co-operative. This doesn't mean that they will not suffer from stress at this time.

Wanting to go home

Anxiety and stress start in hospital when they feel fit enough to return home. They do not accept that they are no longer able to care for themselves. Getting better in a nursing home may show your relatives that they wouldn't be able to manage at home, even with the help of social services. They realise how difficult it is to get up and go to the toilet without help and how hard it is to pick up something that's fallen on the floor. They might begin to wonder how they would cope without being able to call somebody to give them a hand with even the simplest tasks.

If, however, there is any likelihood of them returning home in the future, continuing rehabilitation in a nursing home will make the transition easier. Whatever the outcome, they will suffer from stress.

MANAGING YOUR RELATIVE'S STRESS

There are several ways in which you can help your relative to cope with this stressful period:

- Talk positively to them about the move.
- Emphasise the advantages.
- Ask their friends in to reassure them that they will continue to visit.
- Take them (if possible) to see the home.
- Tell them some of their treasures are already there, waiting for their arrival.
- When matron makes her visit encourage them to ask questions.
- Discuss every step with them.
- Encourage them to help in the preparation for their admission.
- Arrange a trial period before making a permanent commitment.
- Ask the doctor to visit. It's possible he could arrange counselling.

Getting used to their new home – the first hours

It will be much easier for them if you can be at the home when your relative arrives.

On arrival they will be greeted and shown to their room. Most homes offer them and their visitors refreshments when they get there.

Soon afterwards a nurse will come, introduce themselves and chat whilst taking down your relative's personal details.

Later their temperature, pulse, respiration and blood pressure may be taken. A urine sample will probably be required for testing, particularly if they are diabetic. When they get ready for bed it will be noted whether they have any redness of the skin, abrasions or sores. They may also have their weight checked. This is routine and nothing to worry about.

Your relative may have have their photograph taken either when they are admitted or later. This is done in most homes now. The photos are used for identification purposes, particularly by new staff.

Testing has a purpose
These simple tests are done to ensure that they are not suffering from any obvious condition that may need treatment.

Results sometimes lead the nurse to suspect that there could be a problem which will be monitored and reported to the doctor. However, most findings are normal and are used as a base line.

Afterwards their belongings will be unpacked and put away. They may be taken to the lounge and introduced to other residents.

If the chef is available he/she may come and discuss the menu with them.

Naming the faces

There will be many new faces for them to learn and name. Some matrons provide name badges which makes it easier for new residents.

Generally speaking, different categories of staff wear a different colour to make it easier to distinguish who does what.

MEETING THE CARING TEAM

There are five main jobs in a nursing home:

- nursing
- administration (sometimes done by the matron)
- cleaning
- kitchen work
- maintenance.

The people who carry out these jobs work together and constitute a caring team.

Nursing staff

Matron is responsible for:

- the overall running of the home
- ensuring the wellbeing of the residents

- engaging staff
- dealing with complaints and queries
- part or total administration
- many other duties not listed above.

Deputy matron is a Registered General Nurse (RGN) and will take responsibility for the home in matron's absence.

RGNs (Registered General Nurses) are called Sister or Staff Nurse depending on the policy of the home. Residents generally call nurses by their first name. RGNs are responsible to the matron. Their main duty is the total nursing care and wellbeing of the residents. As part of their duties they will:

- supervise all care given to your relative by junior staff
- ensure that they receive all prescribed treatment and medicine
- call a doctor if they are unwell or if they have an accident
- liaise with doctors and other disciplines on their behalf
- note and report to the doctor any adverse affects of drugs
- dress any wounds or sores and carry out prescribed treatments
- do anything necessary to maintain comfort, contentment and good care.

Enrolled Nurses (ENs) are specially trained in bedside nursing and will work alongside both RGNs and care assistants.

Care assistants are special people whom your relative will get to know quite well. They will give them a wash or bath, care for their hair and nails and report any problems to the RGN. Most care assistants are helpful and obliging, often doing extra tasks that contribute to the residents' happiness.

Domestic staff

In larger homes there is a *domestic supervisor*. They are responsible for ensuring the home is kept clean and that all laundry is washed and ironed properly. They may be able to appoint their own domestic and laundry assistants.

Domestic assistants clean your relative's room and all other areas of the home.

Laundry assistants wash, iron, fold and put away all personal items as well as the home laundry.

Kitchen staff

The *chef/cook* is responsible for providing:

- nourishing, appetising meals
- a choice of menu if required
- varied menus
- special diets

The *chef/cook* is also responsible for:

- ordering of food
- cleanliness of all kitchen areas, utensils and equipment
- cleanliness of crockery, cutlery, kitchen and table linen
- maintaining standards as set by the health authority, environmental health and the matron.

Kitchen assistants assist the chef/cook, collect used trays (if used), crockery and cutlery, and sometimes take round hot drinks.

Maintenance engineer/handyman

- is responsible for general maintenance of home and grounds
- carries out some repairs
- informs matron of emergency and major repairs that need to be done
- is involved in safety matters
- subject to matron's approval, will hang pictures or fix shelves *etc* for your relative.

Helping the resident to know who's who

Because there are so many people involved in running a nursing home it may prove confusing for your relative.

- Encourage them to become friendly with another resident who can help them distinguish various people.

- Encourage them to 'learn' one or two of the staff at a time.
- Ask a nurse to explain the staff and their uniforms.
- Find out yourself what the various uniforms mean and leave a list.

CHANGING ROUTINES

Whilst your relative has been living in their own home they have developed their own pattern of living – for example, they may get up at seven o'clock every morning and go to bed at nine o'clock every evening. They will have their meals at a time that suits their lifestyle.

Although all homes have a daily routine it is not inflexible. Within reason residents can rise at the time they prefer and go to bed when they choose.

Meal times

Breakfast is usually between 7.30 and 9 am but other meals are usually at set times. However, if your relative is going out arrangements can be made for them to have their meal at a more convenient time.

Lunchtimes do not usually cause a problem but evening meals may clash with a favourite television programme. Ask the staff if they can have their meal in their room on these occasions.

Keeping clean

Bath days may be different from what they are used to but if your relative speaks to the senior nurse they may be able to compromise so that the new routines are easier for them to cope with. The majority of homes will try to arrange for new residents to have their baths on the same days as they did at home. Continuity of their life pattern helps them adjust to their new surroundings.

HELPING TO EASE THE TRANSITION

Missing and making friends

Your relative will feel neglected if their friends suddenly stop visiting. Try to prevent this by:

- explaining the situation to their friends and fellow members of any church or club

- giving them the new address and times of visiting (it's usually open visiting nowadays)
- making a visiting rota if possible
- asking the staff to encourage your relative to make friends with other residents.

Needing the library

Most homes have a library which is supplied by the local library services. They undertake to change the range of book titles approximately every three months.

Not every home is lucky enough to have this service. In these circumstances you can enrol your relative at the local library and make arrangements to change their books yourself or cajole one of their friends to do it for them.

Shopping

Some matrons organise a 'shopping trolley' catering for simple everyday needs for their residents. Unfortunately, it's not always possible to get volunteers to run such a venture.

Shopping trips are occasionally organised to the local town, especially near Christmas.

In consultation with the matron you may be able to take them yourself using their own or a borrowed wheelchair.

Transport for outings

Some areas have local facilities that provide transport for disabled people, including nursing home residents. For example:

- 'Dial a Ride' (Croydon area)
- 'Compaid' (Tunbridge Wells and Pembury area)

Social services, the local tourist information centre, hospital or council offices may be able to give details.

Needing spiritual fellowship

Practising members of a church will miss the spiritual fellowship given by other church members.

Talk to their vicar, pastor or church leader. They may be able to arrange regular church visiting and/or occasional meetings within the home, subject to an agreement with matron.

Church leaders often have an arrangement whereby they will conduct interdenominational services within the home on a regular basis. Residents of any religion will be visited by a minister of their own faith if they ask matron to arrange it. Communion, if appropriate, can be arranged for individual communicants.

Coping with allergies

Allergies can be caused by anything in the environment. Some people seem to be susceptible to almost everything whilst others do not appear to suffer allergic reactions to anything.

Things that may cause an allergic response

- wasp or insect stings
- change of washing powder
- some foods – strawberries, shell fish *etc*
- aspirin and some other drugs.

Allergies can vary from slight headache to severe respiratory problems.

- If your relative has a known allergy make sure you inform matron.
- If they become unwell in your presence inform the nurse in charge immediately. A doctor or ambulance will be sent for if appropriate.

GETTING THINGS CHANGED

There is a difference between getting things changed and making a complaint, although one thing often leads to the other. For example, if your relative's furniture is not in the most convenience place, discuss with matron the possibility of it being moved to where they want it.

Making a complaint

Whatever the complaint, your relative or you should speak to the nurse in charge at the time it happens. Something simple – for example, the television in the next room is too loud – will be dealt with immediately. Other complaints may take a little longer.

Seeing the right people

If nothing is done about your complaint discuss it with the matron. She will take appropriate steps to redress the situation. Depending on the nature of the complaint it may take a few days to resolve. Matron will inform you about progress or the resolution of the problem.

Approach matron at intervals if the problem is not resolved or no action is taken.

Unresolved complaints

You may feel that your complaint has not been dealt with satisfactorily or that the problem is still there. Make an appointment to see the manager, director or the proprietor. If that's impossible ask them in writing to look into the matter.

Taking it further

If this fails to bring a suitable solution to the problem you should write to the health authority inspectorate for the home who will investigate the complaint on your behalf.

Their address and phone number can be obtained:

- from your relative's contract
- from the local health authority, which is listed in the telephone directory
- from care managers.

Care manager's involvement

If your relative has been placed in the home through a care manager they can discuss the matter with them.

Although care managers do not generally deal with complaints they will speak to the matron or nurse in charge on your relative's behalf.

Should your relative find the situation intolerable they can ask their care manager to suggest more suitable accommodation for them.

CHECKLIST

- Have you discussed your relative's allergies (if any) with matron?
- Have the different colours of uniform been explained?
- Has anybody explained the new routine to your relative?
- Do you know how to make a complaint?

CASE STUDIES

Peter develops a rash

Mavis rang at the door and heard the familiar warning bell go off as it opened. After a few words of greeting with the staff she went in to see her father. He seemed much the same, peering at her as he always did. It was as though he was trying to find memories of her from the deep recesses of his mind.

She was pleased when he reached out to take the sweet she offered. As he stretched his sleeve rode up, exposing a reddened wrist. She took his hand to have a further look but he snatched it away. Mavis then tried to undo his shirt but he became aggressive.

When the nurse came over Mavis pointed out Peter's red wrist and she promised to look at his skin when they took him to the toilet. Mavis stayed until he had been seen. He had developed an irritating rash which was causing him to scratch.

Sister called the doctor, who thought it was an allergic reaction to some new washing powder they had used in the home.

Peggy makes a complaint

Fenella Rough was a domestic assistant responsible for cleaning residents' rooms. She was often rude and bad tempered. Peggy asked for a different domestic to clean her room because she was afraid of Fenella. When Matron asked the reason, Peggy made a formal complaint.

Matron investigated and Fenella received a verbal warning and her duties were changed.

Connie grumbles about the cold

Connie was cold. She had never felt so cold. Now she remembered why she had left England and emigrated to Spain all those years ago. She went to bed cold, shivered all night and got up cold in the morning. If only she could have brought Spanish weather with her.

Audrey came to see her and heard nothing except how cold it was and how she couldn't get warm. She went to see Matron. Connie was given extra blankets. Matron suggested she might like to buy bed socks, a warmer nightdress, and some thermal clothing. There was still time to get to the shops. Connie wouldn't go, it was far too cold for her. Audrey dashed off. She returned laden with clothing warm enough for the Arctic circle! She brought a marking pen with her and once Connie had tried them on she marked them with her name.

MAKING A COMPLAINT

1. Make your complaint to **nurse in charge**

2. If no change, complain to **matron**

3. Still no change, speak to **care manager** (if applicable)
He/she will speak to matron

4. Still no change, see **manager/proprietor**

5. Complaint ignored, put in writing to **manager/proprietor**

6. Complaint still ignored, send a **reminder**

7. Still no response, write to health authority **nursing home inspector**

8. **Inspector** will:

investigate the complaint

discuss it with matron

discuss it with proprietor

Problem resolved.

UNDERSTANDING THE ROLE OF OFFICIAL VISITORS

Fig. 17. Eight steps to making a complaint.

Connie was much warmer with her new 'thermals' and wished she had told Audrey how cold she was before.

Annie is lonely

Annie sat in her room alone thinking of the day Fred had taken a turn for the worse. The nurses had been in constantly to attend to him. Annie had sat, holding his hand, looking on helplessly as she saw his life slowly slip away.

The pastor and several church members had tried to comfort her. The funeral took place at the church where they had worshipped for so many years.

A fortnight passed, none of her friends seemed to come any more. A tear escaped and rolled down her cheek.

Matron noticed the change in Annie and her lack of visitors and telephoned Elizabeth. Elizabeth didn't know but thought it might be because her friends felt embarrassed about visiting somebody so newly bereaved.

Elizabeth spoke to the pastor about the situation. He spoke to those concerned, who promised to go and see Annie again. As fellowship and friendships were renewed Annie was more able to cope with her loss.

DISCUSSION POINTS

1. What will be the best way of preparing your relative for the change in routine?

2. Does your relative need any special diet, for instance, vegetarian?

3. Will your relative's spiritual needs be met easily?

4. Does your relative suffer from any allergies?

11
Seeing New Faces

UNDERSTANDING THE ROLE OF OFFICIAL VISITORS

To prevent standards of care deteriorating, nursing homes are subject to regular inspections by the health authority. The inspectors can visit, unannounced, at any time of the day or night.

Day visits

The inspectors will be taken round by matron or the nurse in charge. However, they may, with matron's permission, wander round the home and speak to the residents unaccompanied.

The objects of their visit are:

- to ensure all residents are being cared for properly
- to see residents are contented
- to give residents and inspectors an opportunity to converse
- to see that there are adequate numbers of staff on duty
- to check staff are of the right skill mix
- to look at menus and inspect kitchens
- to inspect rooms, furniture and bed linen, looking at cleanliness, wear and tear
- to check maintenance of apparatus such as bath hoists and fire equipment
- to ensure fire instruction and practices are carried out
- to check all records, registration and insurance documents
- to examine medicines, storage and medicine record sheets.

As the inspectors walk round the home, staff attitudes and manner towards others, particularly the residents, are noted and recorded. Health inspectors can look at everything to do with the home. They record their findings and if anything causes them concern they act on it immediately. Otherwise, they discuss their findings with matron. Shortly after their visit the matron will receive their written report and recommendations. This is the report mentioned in Chapter 4 in 'The second checklist'.

Night visits

To avoid causing alarm matrons are usually informed that a night visit may take place within a given period – for example, during the next month.

On arrival inspectors must show their official identification card which carries their photograph. They usually take a colleague with them, particularly after dark.

When the inspectors arrive at night, they check that the residents are being cared for, that an adequate number of RGNs and care assistants are on duty, that they are performing their duties properly and conforming to regulations. The visit causes no upheaval and your relative will not even realise they have been.

Environmental health inspectors

These inspectors are seldom seen by residents because they mainly inspect new buildings/extensions and kitchens. They are also involved if there is a problem caused by something in the environment.

Infection control nurse

The nurse will visit if there is an outbreak of an infectious disease, particularly a notifiable disease, such as Legionnaires or salmonella.

They will also visit to update/check methods of cleaning, disinfecting and sterilising. Materials used to prevent infection will be discussed. Recommendations to improve the control of infection in the home are made if necessary.

Police officers

Home beat officers sometimes call in to introduce themselves to the staff and residents. Otherwise, they only come if they are called to investigate an incident – for example, theft, or at the request of the coroner.

The district pharmacist

They are unlikely to be seen by your relative as they are purely concerned with all aspects of ordering, keeping and disposal of residents' medications.

General practitioners and consultants

Doctors visit if they are called by the nursing staff or for routine checks of their patients.

A consultant comes if a domiciliary visit is requested by the doctor.

Representatives and deliveries

Your relative may see representatives visiting the home from time to time. They demonstrate medical equipment, nursing disposables, kitchen and cleaning supplies.

Early risers may see or hear the milkman or other firms making their deliveries.

Maintenance contractors

Although most homes have the services of a handyman there is also a need for maintenance contractors to do specialised work on, for example:

- the boilers (central heating and hot water)
- mobile and bath hoists
- washing machines and dryers
- dishwashers and other equipment
- fire equipment and alarms

COPING WITH A FIRE

If the fire alarms sound without a known cause the nurse in charge will automatically call the fire service out. Staff will start evacuating all residents if there is any suspicion of fire. Even if it proves to be a false alarm fire officers will attend and check the building and suspect alarms.

Periodic fire inspections

These are made by the fire service to check:

- fire hoses
- fire extinguishers, type and maintenance
- fire blankets (mainly used in the kitchens)
- fire doors and escapes – that they are accessible and functional
- smoke alarms, fire alarms and fire notices
- for excess rubbish in the building and blocked fire escapes
- records of fire equipment checks, maintenance of equipment and staff fire drills.

Fire regulations

Fire regulations are laid down by the fire officer. Regular fire inspections are made to see that his instructions are being carried out.

From time to time your relative may see several fire officers wandering about the home. There is no need for alarm. They may be visiting:

- for the orientation of new officers
- to give fire prevention lectures to staff
- because the alarms have sounded.

Alarms can go off due to a fault, insects getting into one of the smoke alarms, somebody smoking underneath a smoke alarm – or due to fire. It is a regulation that fire alarms are deliberately activated weekly. Many matrons prefer to have a set day and time for this job to be done.

Fire lectures and drill have to be carried out at intervals in order that all staff know what to do. Near the fire alarms there will be fire notices telling everybody what to do and what not to do in the event of fire.

Fire regulations stipulate that fire retardant furnishings and bed linen are used.

In the event of fire

- The alarms sound.
- Fire doors with magnetic catches automatically close.
- The fire service is called.

Whilst waiting for the fire service to arrive

- The fire will be located and all doors closed.

- Residents, visitors and staff will go, or be taken, to the assembly point.
- Residents nearest the fire will be moved first.
- A roll-call of residents, visitors and staff will be done.

When the fire service arrive

- They will check the situation.
- They will assist staff to move non-ambulant residents away from danger.
- They will evacuate the building if necessary.
- A roll-call will be made.
- The Health Authority Inspector will be informed.
- In the event of serious damage the residents will be relocated.
- Relocation would be arranged by the inspectors and social services.
- Next of kin would be informed as soon as possible.

Note: Lifts must not be used in the event of fire. Residents, visitors or staff must not stop to pick up valuables.

Visitors' book

Your relative and all visitors will be requested to sign the visitors' book, with the date and time they enter and leave the building. This has a dual purpose:

- Fire officers know who is in the building in the event of fire.
- The security and protection of residents and staff.

CHANGING ROOMS

Occasionally it may become necessary for your relative to change rooms. This may be due to:

- emergency repairs – for example, leaking radiator
- general maintenance – for example, redecoration
- deterioration in health requiring more supervision
- a wish to upgrade or downgrade their room

- room proving unsuitable for their needs.

Unless the move is due to emergency repairs your relative and you will be consulted and shown the alternative room.

Assuming that the move is approved the staff will transfer them and all their belongings to their new room.

If the change is due to emergency repairs or general maintenance they will return to their original room once the work is completed. However, if they prefer the new room they could try and negotiate a permanent change with the matron.

LIVING THROUGH THE DEATH OF A PARTNER

It's not uncommon for married couples to be admitted into a nursing home where they can share a room and be cared for together.

When one of the partners passes away it causes understandable pain and problems for the widow(er).

- They can't bear to see the bed occupied by somebody else.
- They don't want their partner's possessions moved.
- They become aggressive to anybody else sleeping in his/her bed.
- They don't want to change their room nor do they want to share.
- They won't allow his/her bed to be changed for another.
- They can't afford to keep the double room as a single.

The best solution tends to be to persuade them to transfer to a single room if possible. They will not like the idea. Try to convince them that it will be better for them by:

- taking them to see the room a few times
- telling them how much nicer the room is
- reminding them of the privacy a single room will give them
- getting them to plan how they would like to have it arranged
- explaining that it is much less expensive than the double room.

CHECKLIST

- Are you familiar with the fire regulations?
- Does your relative understand the procedure in the event of fire?
- Do you know where the fire alarms are and how to use them?
- Have you found out where the fire exits are?

CASE STUDIES

Somebody leaves the tap on

Peter and the other residents were sitting in the lounge when there was a shriek from one of the staff. Water was pouring out of Peter's room and about to start cascading down the stairs.

The tap was turned off quickly and mopping up began. Peter's room was saturated: his carpet squelched as staff walked across the room.

Matron decided to move Peter into another room. Although he was told he did not understand. The nurses moved his belongings and the senior nurse phoned Mavis to inform her of the temporary change.

A week passed before the room was ready to be used again. Mavis and Julia preferred the new room as it was on the ground floor. The outlook was more stimulating too. It hadn't been available when Peter was admitted.

Mavis spoke to matron, who agreed that Peter could stay in the new room.

Peggy hears the fire alarm

Peggy had not been told that the fire alarms were tested every Tuesday morning. She heard the strident ringing of the bell, just outside her room, and heard the thuds as the automatic catches released the doors. She guessed it was the fire alarms. Panic beset her. Would they get her out in time? With her good hand she pressed the call bell. A nurse came quickly.

When Peggy told her about her fear, the nurse reassured her that if there had been a fire she would have been evacuated to safety in time. She then told her it was a routine alarm check and apologised for not telling her that the alarms were tested every week.

Connie sees the fire brigade

Connie was surprised to see a fire tender in the drive. Going along to the lounge she saw six fire officers in the corridor. She passed them, smelling the smoky odour of their protective clothing. Her hands automatically went to smooth her hair and she glanced in the mirror as she went by.

Later she saw the officers leave and asked why they had come. She was told that they had come to familiarise some new staff with the layout of the building.

Annie moves into a single room

After several weeks matron thought Annie might like company. Unfortunately, Annie couldn't bear to see anybody sleeping in Fred's bed or sitting in 'his' chair. She was asked if she would like to move to another room but she didn't. Something had to be done.

Matron contacted CRUSE - an organisation that helps the bereaved. A CRUSE member befriended Annie and helped her cope with her grief, visiting frequently at first, then at longer intervals.

After the funeral Annie had decided she didn't want to go back to 'their' home again - not without Fred.

Matron told her that she had another couple needing a double room and asked if she would move to a single room. Annie capitulated and said she would go and see it.

Elizabeth came and took her to the new room, on the other side of the house. Although Annie was still sad she liked the room and decided to move into it. This proved to be a turning point. Within a few weeks she became involved with the weekly activity programme once again.

DISCUSSION POINTS

1. If your relatives are married, plan what to do if one partner dies.

2. How much should your relative be told about fire procedure?

3. If for any reason your relative had to change rooms, how would it affect them?

Glossary

Accident book form. Book or form used for recording accidents to residents, visitors or staff.

Ambiguous. Difficult to understand.

Ambulant. Able to walk about from place to place.

Assembly point. Designated place where all staff, residents and visitors assemble in the event of fire alarms sounding.

Assessing needs. Estimating the amount of help a person requires to enable them to live as normal a life as possible.

Back rest. An appliance to support a person when they are sitting up in bed.

Baseline. Normal temperature, pulse *etc* for a particular individual.

Bed cradle. An appliance for relieving the weight of bedclothes off a person in bed.

BS 5750. British Standard of Quality.

Care manager. A person who will assist in assessing care and financial needs of a prospective resident.

Care plan. A detailed ongoing plan of action to ensure a resident's needs/problems are noted and attended to. Care plans are reviewed and updated regularly.

Charitable organisation. An institution set up to provide help to needy people.

Colostomy. A surgically made opening between the colon and the surface of the abdomen which acts as an artificial anus.

Commode. A type of chair that conceals a toilet.

Complaints procedure. How to make a complaint.

Contract. A formal agreement between two parties – for example, the resident and the home.

Contracted fee. The agreed fees charged by the home and written in the contract.

CRUSE. An organisation that helps bereaved people.

Deposit. A sum of money put down to secure a bed or room until the person can be admitted.

DHSS/DSS. Department of Social Security.

Diet. A specific allowance or selection of food. Various diets can be used for different complaints – for instance, reducing for overweight person.

Disclaimer. A denial of any claim.

Domiciliary visit. A visit from the doctor/consultant to a patient's home.

Dual registration. A home registered to give residential and nursing care within the same establishment or complex.

Electric wheelchair. A wheelchair powered by rechargeable batteries.

EMI home. Home registered to care for the Elderly Mentally Ill resident.

EN. A trained Enrolled Nurse.

Evacuation procedure. Method of withdrawing all persons from the home in event of fire.

Exacerbate. An increase in the severity of symptoms.

Fluid balance chart. A record of a person's fluid intake (drinks) and output (urine *etc*).

Geriatrician. A doctor who specialises in the diagnosis and treatment of illnesses affecting elderly people.

GP. General practitioner (doctor).

Grant. One-off or recurrent sums of money given to a person in need.

Helping hand. An appliance used as a hand extension for reaching items.

Infection control nurse. A nurse who specialises in the control of infections. They are usually employed by the health authority but visit and advise in the event of a widespread or dangerous infection within a nursing home.

Jigsaw puzzle folding tray. A tray designed for jigsaw enthusiasts which folds with an unfinished puzzle within it.

Key worker. A nurse who is allocated to care for the same residents on a regular basis. They will generally have one or two care assistants in their team.

Music and movement. Gentle exercise to music. People with pacemakers should seek medical advice before joining in.

Nausea. A feeling of sickness without actually vomiting.

Norton score. A scoring system of assessing a patient's susceptibility to pressure sores.

Nursing home charter. A document setting out the nursing home's commitment to their residents.

Nursing home inspectors. Inspectors appointed by the health authority to register nursing homes, to uphold and improve standards by making regular inspections and to investigate complaints.

NVQ. National Vocational Qualification: a training programme combining practical work, lectures, and assessments.

Occupational therapy. The therapeutic use of crafts or hobbies particularly in the rehabilitation of patients.

Pacemaker. A device fitted to regulate the heart beat.

Paint pen. A paint filled fibre tipped pen: useful for marking plastic, wood or metal items.

Parker bath. A specially designed bath allowing easy access for the frail and/or disabled person. The side is made to rise for entry and is then locked into place whilst the bath is in use.

Prescription. Issued by the doctor for medication. NHS prescriptions are filled on production of the statutory payment or free to certain categories of patients (age 60 plus). Privately issued prescriptions are not exempt from payment. The full cost has to be borne by the patient.

Pressure sore. A sore caused mainly by prolonged local pressure being exerted on the body at various points. For example, by blankets or other items causing pressure, or by prolonged sitting or lying in the same position.

Prognosis. The outcome of an illness or disease.

Prosthesis. Artificial substitute of a missing or damaged part of the body (limbs, dentures, eyes *etc*).

Registered categories. The classification of resident a home is registered to care for. For example: EMI, residential nursing *etc*.

Registration certificate. Registered homes are issued with a certificate by the Nursing Home Inspection Department. It shows the categories of resident they are allowed to admit.

Rehabilitation. Helping a person to regain their former abilities.

Remission. A period of abatement of symptoms in a disease, for example multiple sclerosis.

RGN/RN. Registered General Nurse sometimes known as Registered Nurse.

Relocation. Moving a resident from their room to another, either temporarily or permanently.

RMN. Registered Mental Nurse.

Self funding. A resident who pays their own fees without seeking income support.

Skill mix. The ratio of trained nurses to care assistants.

Snagging. Repairing plaster cracks and other minor faults that appear during the first few months of a new building's life. The builders generally return to do the work after about six months.

Spenco mattress. A soft washable mattress used in addition to the usual one to help prevent pressure sores developing.

Top up. An extra fee, asked for by a few homes, to bring the DSS or contracted fees into line with self-funded residents. Care managers should be informed if this is asked for.

Tripod. A walking aid.

Walking frame. A walking aid used by people who can use both arms. Usually known as a Zimmer frame.

Useful Addresses

Age Concern England, Astral House, 1268 London Road, Norbury, London SW16 4ER. Tel: (0181) 679 8000.

Alzheimer's Disease Society, 158/160 Balham High Road, London SW12 9BN. Tel: (0181) 675 6657.

Arthritis and Rheumatism Council, Copeman House, St Mary's Court, St Mary's Place, Castlefield, Derbyshire S41 7TD. Tel: (0171) 405 8752.

British Colostomy Association, 113-115 Station Road, Reading, Berkshire RG1 1LG. Tel: (01734) 391537.

British Deaf Association, 38 Victoria Place, Carlisle CA1 1HU. Tel: (01228) 48844.

British Diabetic Association, 10 Queen Anne Street, London W1M 0BD Tel: (0171) 323 1531.

British Heart Foundation, 14 Fitzhardinge Street, London W1H 4DH. Tel: (0171) 935 0185.

Counsel and Care for the Aged, Twyman House, Lower Ground Floor, 16 Bonny Street, London NW91 9PG. Tel: (0171) 485 1566.

Disabled Living Foundation, 380-384 Harrow Road, London W9 2HU. Tel: (0171) 289 6111.

Help the Aged, Housing and Care Division, 7 Muster Green, Haywards Heath RH16 4AP. Tel: (01444) 441018.

Hi Centre West Kent, Deaf/Hearing Impaired People, 3 Castle Street, Tonbridge, Kent TN9 1BH. Tel: (01732) 773060.

Incontinence Advisory Service, 380-384 Harrow Road, London W9 2HU. Tel: (0171) 289 6111 Monday – Thursday.

MIND National Association for Mental Health, 22 Harley Street, London W1N 2ED. Tel: (0171) 637 0741.

Mobility Trust, 4 Hughes Mews, 143 Chatham Road, London SW1 16H. Tel: (0171) 924 3597.

MS Society of Great Britain, 25 Effie Road, Fulham, London SW6 1EE. Tel: (0171) 737 6267.

Parkinson's Disease Society, 22 Upper Woburn Place, London WC1H 0RA. Tel: (0171) 383 3513.

Stroke Association, 123-127 White Cross Street, London EC1Y 8JJ. Tel: (0171) 490 7999.

Further Reading

BENEFITS AGENCY LEAFLETS

No. FB 2: *Which benefit?*
No. IS 50: *Income Support – help if you live in residential care home or nursing home.*
No. NI 196: *Social Security benefit rates.*

Obtainable from your local Social Security Office (Benefits Agency) or by post from:

HMSO
Oldham Broadway Business Park
Broadgate
Chadderton
Oldham OL9 0JA.

GRANTS

A Guide to Grants for Individuals in Need, edited by David Casson and Paul Brown (a Directory of Social Change publication).

OTHER TITLES IN THE 'HOW TO' SERIES

Dealing with a Death in the Family, Sylvia Murphy (How To Books, 1997).
How to Claim State Benefits, Martin Rathfelder (How To Books, 3rd edition 1995).
Making a Complaint, Helen Shay (How To Books, 1996).
Managing Your Personal Finances, John Claxton (How To Books, 1996).
Successful Grandparenting, Doris Corti (How To Books, 1997).

Index

HOW TO CLAIM STATE BENEFITS
A practical guide for claimants and advisers

Martin Rathfelder

The Welfare State changes all the time. The third edition of this book has been completely rewritten to take full account of the abolition of the poll tax, mobility allowance, invalidity benefit and unemployment benefit, and the introduction of council tax, disability living allowance, incapacity benefit and jobseeker's allowance – as well as many minor changes. It is the only popular paperback which explains the whole range of benefits available from local and central government, showing you exactly how to claim, and how to arrange your affairs to take advantage of the current benefit system.

160pp illus. 1 85703 073 7. 3rd edition.

SUCCESSFUL GRANDPARENTING
How to manage family and practical issues

Doris Corti

The average life expectancy is increasing. More people are likely to experience the joys and sorrows of being a grandparent for a longer period of their life. Being a grandparent is different to being a parent. Expectations are different. Many grandparents find that the requirements for bringing up children in today's changing world are very different to what was the norm when they were parents. This new book gives practical advice on such diverse aspects as finances, housing, child-minding, taking the role of step-grandparent, sharing grandchildren's upbringing, diplomacy, and obtaining access to children when parents separate or divorce. The answers to these and other problems are given in this book, as well as the names and addresses of helpful organisations. As well as grandparents, typical readers of this book will include grandparents-to-be, retirement groups, library readers, counsellors in church organisations and citizen advice bureaux. Doris Corti has three grandchildren and is an active member of the Grandparents Association.

160pp illus. 1 85703 307 8.

MAKING A COMPLAINT

How to put your case successfully and win redress

Helen Shay

Whether you've bought faulty shoes or been sold an unsuitable investment; been over-charged by a bank or suffered the holiday from hell; this book guides you through the maze of complaints procedures, courts, ombudsmen and other forms of consumer redress. It makes the law user-friendly and shows you how to obtain compensation – fast. It shows the way to cut through the aggravation and achieve the best solution for you. Helen Shay is a solicitor of twelve years' standing. She has worked both in private practice and as an in-house lawyer for a major high street retailer – so has experience of consumer disputes from both sides. Currently with an ombudsman's office, she is well-versed in current consumer issues and the problems which can confront the individual versus large organisations. She also tutors and lectures part-time in commercial law, and is knowledgeable in contract, consumer credit, banking law, conveyancing and other legal areas affecting everyday life.

128pp illus. 1 85703 102 4.

TAKING IN STUDENTS

How to make your spare room pay

Rosemary Bartholomew

Extra cash is always useful to any householder, so why not put your spare room to work for you? There is always a need for short and longer term accommodation, particularly for young people. As well as those simply looking for somewhere to live, there are also various organisations – private and statutory – which are constantly in need of temporary lodgings for their students or staff. Written by an experienced landlady this book explains some of the options you could consider, gives useful information about what to expect, and includes many helpful hints and money-saving tips. Rosemary Bartholomew is a registered language school hostess and private landlady. Her wide variety of guests and lodgers have stayed for periods of anything from one week to five years.

128pp illus. 1 85703 323 X.

CASH FROM YOUR COMPUTER

How to sell word-processing, book-keeping, desktop publishing and other services

Zoe King

As a computer owner, you know that you use your computer to just a fraction of its real capacity. Now, with the help of this book, you can capitalise on a major asset which spends most of its time sitting idly on your desk. This book tells you everything you need to know about selling your services in the fields of word-processing, desktop publishing, book-keeping and a great deal more. You'll find advice on unusual sources of extra income, as well as help in choosing the most appropriate and cost-effective software and hardware. Here at last is a computer user's book which will help you take advantage of *all* the money-making potentials open to you. Zoe King was until recently the Sales and Marketing Director of a computer software company. She is a freelance writer and editor, who has for several years supplemented her income by offering computer services to local companies, charities, and individuals.

128pp illus. 1 85703 338 8.

MAKING A WEDDING SPEECH

Choosing the right words for every occasion

John Bowden

At thousands of weddings each year, many people are called on to 'say a few words'. But what do you say? How do you find the right words which will go down really well with the assembled company? Written by an experienced and qualified public speaker, this entertaining book shows you how to put together a simple but effective speech well suited to the particular occasion. Whether you are the best man, bridegroom, father of the bride or other participant, it will guide you every step from great opening lines to apt quotations, anecdotes, tips on using humour, and even contains 50 short model speeches you can use or adapt to any occasion.

160pp 1 85703 347 7. 3rd edition.

MANAGING YOUR PERSONAL FINANCES
How to achieve financial security and survive the shrinking welfare state

John Claxton

Life for most people has become increasingly beset by financial worries, and meanwhile the once-dependable prop of state help is shrinking. Today's financial world is a veritable jungle full of predators after your money. This book will help you to check your financial health and prepare a strategy towards creating your own welfare state and financial independence. Find out in simple language with many examples and case studies how to avoid debt, how to finance your home, how to prepare for possible incapacity or redundancy and how to finance your retirement, including care in old age. Discover how to acquire new financial skills, increase your income, reduce outgoings, and prepare to survive in a more self-reliant world. John Claxton is a chartered management accountant and chartered secretary; he teaches personal money management in adult education.

160pp illus. 1 85703 328 0.

HELPING YOUR CHILD TO READ
How to prepare the child of today for the world of tomorrow

Jonathan Myers

Would you like your child to be able to read well? How do you support your child's reading – at school and at home? Who do you ask for advice? What games and activities are useful? What should you look for when buying books? When does a reading problem need expert attention? How do you check your child's progress? In our fast moving, computerised world, reading is absolutely vital. It is the key basic skill that children and adults need to transmit information. And reading is fun too. With its lively text, examples and case studies, this forward looking book shows how easy it is for you to get your child on the right road to reading success. Jonathan Myers BSc PGCE is an educational consultant and teacher specialising in reading development, dyslexia and a wide range of associated problems.

141pp illus. 1 85703 192 X.

SUCCESSFUL SINGLE PARENTING

How to combine bringing up children with your own life goals

Mike Lilley

In the United Kingdom there as now 1.4 million one-parent families, with 2.2 million children, one out of five families. There are many routes into single parenthood, all of them are difficult to face. However you get there as a single parent, the job of bringing up children alone is very demanding. You have to learn to cope with becoming the only bread-winner of the family as well as taking care of the emotional and physical needs of your children. This new book offers some practical ways to ease the hard road of single parenting: it will not take away the isolation and loneliness but it will provide a checklist of the problems you may face and provide ways to overcome them whether emotional, financial, or legal. Mike Lilley is a single parent of three children and a leading spokesperson on the issue of one-parent families, appearing regularly on TV and radio. He founded and edited the first national newsstand magazine for single parents *Singled Out.*

160pp illus. 1 85703 302 7.

HOW TO RUN A VOLUNTARY GROUP

A guide to successful organisation and management

Chris Carling

Could you manage a small group of voluntary workers? Would you like to see better results being achieved from everyone's efforts? If so, this book is for you. Making use of realistic case studies throughout, it shows how to set up a voluntary group or re-organise one, how to keep proper records, take decisions and get things done, how to manage individual volunteers, how to manage fund-raising and budgets, how to manage time effectively, how to cope with typical common problems, how to stay within the law, and even how to employ paid staff. Complete with step-by-step tips and helpful checklists. 'Ideal for the novice organiser'. *Birmingham Voluntary Service Council.* A graduate of Exeter and Cambridge Universities, Chris Carling is a member of the Women's Committee of the Writers Guild, and Chair of the Cambridge Mediation Service.

160pp 1 85703 135 0.

WINNING CONSUMER COMPETITIONS
How to scoop valuable cash and other prizes time and time again

Kathy Kantypowicz

The definitive guide to winning competitions, this volume will show you how you too can stake your claim to some of the millions of glittering prizes offered to consumers every year. Learn how to find entry forms, research your answers and, most important of all, write those few well chosen tie-breaker words which can scoop cars, family holidays, household appliances, clothing, TV and hi-fi equipment, cash and almost any other luxury item you care to name. Why buy when you can win? This book may revolutionize your shopping habits forever. It's easy and it's fun to be a winner! Kathy Kantypowicz has won wore than £200,000 worth of prizes and is dubbed 'The Queen of Competitions' by the British press. Now editor of *Competitors World* magazine, she was formerly resident competition expert on *The Big Breakfast Show* and has appeared regularly in television, press and radio features.

120pp illus. 1 85703 333 7.

HOW TO PLAN A WEDDING
A guide to all aspects of preparation

Mary Kilborn

Expertly written by a former counsellor with the Scottish Marriage Guidance Council, this book fills the need for a practical guide on the questions every couple or their parents need to consider. With lots of helpful headings, and quick checklists, the book covers getting engaged, buying the ring, making announcements, wedding ceremonies and marriage vows, organising the reception, speeches, gifts, honeymoon arrangements and more. The book also contains helpful advice on such things as mixed marriages, the pregnant bride, how to cope with divorced parents, and even how to get married on a beach in the Bahamas. With specimen invitation cards, wedding lists, useful contacts, and more. This latest edition has been fully revised to take account of the 1994 Marriage Act. 'Recommended reading' *Northern Echo.*

128pp illus. 1 85703 154 7. 3rd edition.

How To Books

___ Selling into Japan (£14.99)
___ Setting up Home in Florida (£9.99)
___ Spend a Year Abroad (£8.99)
___ Start a Business from Home (£7.99)
___ Start a New Career (£6.99)
___ Starting to Manage (£8.99)
___ Starting to Write (£8.99)
___ Start Word Processing (£8.99)
___ Start Your Own Business (£8.99)
___ Study Abroad (£8.99)
___ Study & Learn (£7.99)
___ Study & Live in Britain (£7.99)
___ Studying at University (£8.99)
___ Studying for a Degree (£8.99)
___ Successful Grandparenting (£8.99)
___ Successful Mail Order Marketing (£9.99)
___ Successful Single Parenting (£8.99)
___ Survive at College (£4.99)
___ Survive Divorce (£8.99)
___ Surviving Redundancy (£8.99)
___ Take Care of Your Heart (£5.99)
___ Taking in Students (£8.99)
___ Taking on Staff (£8.99)
___ Taking Your A-Levels (£8.99)
___ Teach Abroad (£8.99)
___ Teach Adults (£8.99)
___ Teaching Someone to Drive (£8.99)
___ Travel Round the World (£8.99)
___ Use a Library (£6.99)
___ Use the Internet (£9.99)
___ Winning Consumer Competitions (£8.99)
___ Winning Presentations (£8.99)
___ Work from Home (£8.99)
___ Work in an Office (£7.99)
___ Work in Retail (£8.99)
___ Work with Dogs (£8.99)
___ Working Abroad (£14.99)
___ Working as a Holiday Rep (£9.99)
___ Working in Japan (£10.99)
___ Working in Photography (£8.99)
___ Working in the Gulf (£10.99)
___ Working on Contract Worldwide (£9.99)
___ Working on Cruise Ships (£9.99)
___ Write a CV that Works (£7.99)
___ Write a Press Release (£9.99)
___ Write a Report (£8.99)
___ Write an Assignment (£8.99)
___ Write an Essay (£7.99)
___ Write & Sell Computer Software (£9.99)
___ Write Business Letters (£8.99)
___ Write for Publication (£8.99)
___ Write for Television (£8.99)
___ Write Your Dissertation (£8.99)
___ Writing a Non Fiction Book (£8.99)
___ Writing & Selling a Novel (£8.99)
___ Writing & Selling Short Stories (£8.99)
___ Writing Reviews (£8.99)
___ Your Own Business in Europe (£12.99)

To: Plymbridge Distributors Ltd, Plymbridge House, Estover Road, Plymouth PL6 7PZ.
Customer Services Tel: (01752) 202301. Fax: (01752) 202331.

Please send me copies of the titles I have indicated. Please add postage & packing (UK £1, Europe including Eire, £2, World £3 airmail).

☐ I enclose cheque/PO payable to Plymbridge Distributors Ltd for £ ____________

☐ Please charge to my ☐ MasterCard, ☐ Visa, ☐ AMEX card.

Account No. ☐☐☐☐☐☐☐☐☐☐☐☐☐☐☐☐

Card Expiry Date ☐☐ 19☐ ☎ **Credit Card orders may be faxed or phoned.**

Customer Name (CAPITALS) ....

Address ....

.... Postcode ....

Telephone .... Signature ....

Every effort will be made to despatch your copy as soon as possible but to avoid possible disappointment please allow up to 21 days for despatch time (42 days if overseas). Prices and availability are subject to change without notice.

Code BPA